Sullivan

wishes you

well in your

professional endeavors

to help children

Janet M

Children: Stress, Trauma and Disasters

Jon A. Shaw
Zelde Espinel
James M. Shultz

MILLER
SCHOOL OF MEDICINE
UNIVERSITY OF MIAMI

DEEP
center
Disaster & Extreme Event Preparedness

Table of Contents

Children:
Stress,
Trauma &
Disasters

Children: Stress, Trauma and Disasters

Published by
Disaster Life Support Publishing
Tampa Florida

Library of Congress Cataloguing in Publication Data

Shaw, Jon A.; Espinel, Zelde; Shultz, James M.
Children: Stress, Trauma and Disaster
Includes bibliographical references

ISBN 978-0-9794061-2-6 (hardback)

1. Psychic trauma in children.
2. Disasters—Psychological aspects.
3. Terrorism—Psychological aspects.
4. Posttraumatic stress disorder in children.

Children: Stress, Trauma and Disasters

Jon A. Shaw, M.D.
Professor of Clinical Psychiatry & Behavioral Sciences
Chief, Child and Adolescent Psychiatry Division
Department of Psychiatry and Behavioral Sciences
University of Miami Miller School of Medicine
Miami, Florida

Zelde Espinel, M.D., M.A., M.P.H.
Co-Director
Center for Disaster & Extreme Event Preparedness
(DEEP Center)
Department of Epidemiology & Public Health
University of Miami Miller School of Medicine
Miami, Florida

James M. Shultz, M.S., Ph.D.
Director
Center for Disaster & Extreme Event Preparedness
(DEEP Center)
Department of Epidemiology & Public Health
University of Miami Miller School of Medicine
Miami, Florida

INTRODUCTION

Children: Stress, Trauma and Disasters

One out of every four children experiences a significant traumatic event before reaching adulthood (Costello et al., 2002). While chance, geography and other variables determine risk, all of us are confronted with threats to well-being or even to life itself as we move across the life cycle. The world has become increasingly dangerous.

Disasters, whether natural or human-generated, involve an encounter between forces of harm and a human population in harm's way, in which the demands of the situation exceed the coping capacity of the affected population (Shultz et al., 2007; WHO, 1992). We hear almost daily the horrific accounts of the effects of natural disasters and extreme events including earthquakes, monsoonal rains, flooding, tornadoes, hurricanes, droughts, and global warming. As if the "acts of nature" were not enough, we increasingly see the derivative effects of human-generated violence. Wars, civil strife, ethnic conflict and acts of terrorism encircle the globe and only few seem safe from such possible happenings. Millions of children are growing up in families and communities torn apart by armed conflict. It has been reported that two million children have been killed in wars, five million have been disabled and 12 million have been left homeless (UNICEF, 1997). Acts of terrorism against our homeland have occurred in recent history and will occur again. The child's psychological reactions to disaster, and the responses of the family, are shaped by the distinguishing features and unique forces inherent in each type of disaster.

This book is an effort to bring together our understanding of the effects of stress, traumatic events and disaster on children and their families. While children are generally exposed to the same spectrum of hazards as adults, they are still maturing physically, emotionally, cognitively and socially. Thus, the impact of perceived threat or physical harm must be understood in terms of the child's developmental level and also within the family and social context within which the child lives.

We begin by defining terms essential to understanding the psychological effects of trauma exposure such as stress, primary and secondary stressors, the acute traumatic moment and traumatic reminders. We will see that the child's psychological response to trauma exposure is influenced by a complex array of contextual factors operating at individual, family, community and societal levels. For children, individual factors include age, gender, race, educational level, medical and psychiatric history, trauma history and the child's level of functioning before and during the disaster. Family factors such as family structure and cohesiveness, communication patterns, parental response to disaster impact and post-disaster family functioning are powerful predictors of the child's response. Salient community and societal factors include culture, ethnicity, socioeconomic status, social support networks and post-disaster community functioning.

When a community and its children are impacted by disaster, some definable groups of children will require additional, customized or specialized approaches to assure their protection and to facilitate their recovery from the extreme event (Flynn, 2006). Children with special needs include those who are developmentally disabled, children who are medically or psychiatrically ill, children living in poverty, foster care children and children who have suffered from repetitive exposure to interpersonal violence or maltreatment.

When mass casualties occur in a disaster, survivors are exposed to scenes of death. Death from disaster usually occurs suddenly and unexpectedly, striking down the healthy and taking life prematurely. Children may experience the death of parents, siblings or close friends. Children's early exposure to death, the discovery that life is not permanent, the realization that the body is susceptible to harm, and the loss of important, care-giving relationships in their daily lives, are traumatic experiences. Children suffer not only from the premature loss of a family member, but also from exposure to the cruel and violent nature of the death. Psychological and physiological reactions to bereavement are processed differently in children compared with adults because of the child's cognitive, emotional, and physical immaturity. Various strategies for support and intervention for the bereaved child will be discussed.

Children:
Stress,
Trauma &
Disasters

To confront the psychological consequences of trauma exposure and to optimize recovery, timely assessment and intervention are essential to mitigate the child's risk for ongoing distress, impairment and psychiatric illness. We discuss the parameters for providing careful and ongoing assessment of children's psychological reactions to disaster and trauma. As research on traumatized children and their families has increased, so has the level of thoughtfulness regarding psychosocial interventions to facilitate recovery. Psychological First Aid is a promising early intervention, implemented in the immediate aftermath of disaster, designed to reduce the initial distress and foster adaptive coping for survivors of all ages (NCTSN/NCPTSD, 2006). Effective intervention restores function and enhances recovery; creates a safe and secure environment; reduces uncertainty, fear and anxiety; and mobilizes family and social supports. Evidence-based empirical studies have begun to define the most effective interventions for use throughout the post-impact period to sustain long-term recovery.

Working with children exposed to traumatic events is emotionally demanding and "gut wrenching" in its painful confrontation with the child's lost innocence and premature exposure to the uncertain realties of life threat and the inevitable losses that are part of the life cycle. This book is an effort to facilitate an understanding of that process so that we may be more able to support children and their families as they cope and adapt to stress, disasters and traumatic life experiences.

CH 1

Stress and Trauma

Chapter 1

Stress and Trauma

On successful completion of this chapter you should be able to:

1) Define and differentiate the concepts of stress, stressor, and traumatic stress
2) Compare and contrast the spectrum of stressors
3) Recognize the physiological basis of the stress response
4) Identify acute and chronic effects of stress
5) Define traumatic reminder

Key Concepts

- Children and adolescents are exposed to various types of stress and traumatic events during their developmental years.
- How you define a situation determines your emotional response.
- Primary or acute stressors are relatively circumscribed in time and space.
- Secondary or chronic stressors derive from long-term and continuing exposure.
- A traumatic event occurs when an individual experiences, witnesses or is confronted with a situation in which there is a perceived or real threat of bodily injury or a threat to life itself.
- The acute traumatic moment for the child is frequently ushered in by the discovery that parents are not able to protect them and there is a sudden awareness of vulnerability in the presence of imminent physical injury or death.
- The individual response to stress is shaped by the reality of the impact of the fateful event and by one's subjective appraisal.
- Traumatic reminders refer to those events in the aftermath of traumatic exposure which result in the child or adolescent reliving and re-experiencing the trauma as if it was occurring one more time.

Introduction

Throughout the course of the life cycle, all of us are confronted with threats to well-being or even to life itself. Although children are generally exposed to the same spectrum of hazards as adults, they are still maturing physically, emotionally, cognitively and socially. Therefore, the impact of perceived threat, psychological trauma, or overt physical harm may become woven into the tapestry of their emergent personalities and their repertoire of adapting and coping capacities. In this chapter we will define terms essential to understanding the psychological effects of trauma exposure: stress, acute and chronic stressors, primary and secondary stressors, traumatic event, acute traumatic moment, and traumatic reminders.

Stress

Stress is a non-specific response of the body to any demand placed upon the organism. Stress can be defined as a real or imagined threat to the psychological or physical integrity of the self, a threat to one's equilibrium or homeostasis. Stress represents an incongruity between the individual's adaptive capacities and the demands placed on the organism (Taylor & Fraser, 1981). The child's level of emotional and cognitive development greatly influences the psychological response to events in which demands exceed capacities.

It is important to understand the role of subjective appraisal in responding to stress. From a cognitive perspective, stress, like beauty, is often in the eye of the beholder. How one defines a situation determines one's emotional response to it. Indeed, a situation that one person might perceive as stressful may be experienced by another person as an interesting challenge. As John Milton observed, "The mind is a place in and of itself, it can make a heaven of hell or a hell of heaven." If you define something as real, it is real in its consequences.

Stress

- Stress is the subjective experience that occurs when we perceive that the demands of the situation exceed our resources to successfully cope with those demands
- Stress may be in the eye of the beholder

The Spectrum of Stressors

Stressors are events and situations that prompt and provoke the stress response. Stressors will be presented from three vantage points: stressors in the human experience, primary versus secondary stressors, and acute versus chronic stressors.

Stressors in the human experience. From the perspective of the human experience, stressors are intrinsic to important milestones in the life cycle. Life developmental stressors include such events as childbirth, birth of a sibling, early parent death, separation from loved ones, family discord, divorce, aging, hospitalization, surgery, and physical illnesses. Children who are exposed to such stressors may exhibit clearly discernable behavior changes. For example, a school-age boy who experiences the sudden unexpected death of his father may resume bedwetting, became afraid to sleep alone and cling to his mother, insisting that he does not want to go to school.

Natural disasters include weather-related events (hurricanes, tornadoes, and floods), seismic events (earthquakes, tsunamis, and volcanoes), droughts and pandemics. **Human-generated disasters** may be subdivided into non-intentional versus intentional events (Shultz et al., 2007). Non-intentional, human-generated incidents include transportation crashes, hazardous materials spills, and structural collapses, reflecting accidental failures of human technologies. In other instances, harm is clearly intended during acts of aggression toward individuals (child maltreatment, assault, rape, torture) and acts of mass violence (war, civil strife, ethnic conflict, and terrorism).

Table 1.1 Stressors in the Human Experience

Life/Developmental Stressors	Disasters and Acts of Violence	
	Natural Disasters	Human-generated Events

• Childbirth
• Birth of a sibling
• Early parent death
• Separation from loved ones
• Family discord
• Accidents
• Financial problems
• Divorce
• Hospitalization
• Surgery
• Physical illness
• Unemployment
• Aging
	• Hurricanes
	• Tornadoes
	• Earthquakes
	• Floods
	• Pandemics
	• Tsunamis
	• Wildfires
		Unintentional events
		  • Transportation and industrial
		    disasters
		  • Hazardous materials events
		
		Intentional events
		  • Terrorism
		  • War
		  • Civil or ethnic conflict
		  • Sexual abuse
		  • Child maltreatment
		  • Torture
		  • Aggressive assaults

Primary stressors are associated with acute threats to well-being, physical harm or life-threat to self or loved ones. Primary stressors are associated with direct exposure to the forces of harm during an episode of interpersonal violence or during the period of disaster impact. **Secondary stressors** occur subsequent to a primary stressor as a cluster of consequences or adversities encountered in the aftermath of a traumatic event.

For example, a child who is accidentally burned by scalding water (primary stressor) may experience a multiplicity of secondary stressors including hospitalization, severe pain, surgical procedures, debridement, scarring and disfigurement, separation from parents, interruption of school attendance, and disruption of daily routines including play activities and socialization.

At the community level, the coastal landfall of a strong hurricane will subject the population in the impact zone to such primary stressors as ravaging winds, storm surge, and torrential rainfall. While the impact phase of the hurricane is brief (hours to days), the storm's aftermath may produce a succession of secondary stressors including disruption of power and utilities, shortages of basic necessities, damage to home, displacement, repair delays, loss of

valued possessions, school closures, and disruption of health care services, unemployment, and economic crisis. Following Hurricane Andrew, 25 percent of families moved out of the impact zone. Many children discovered that their schools were closed and some of their closest friends had moved away (Shaw et al., 1995). Similarly, Hurricane Katrina was associated with massive displacement and out-migration from New Orleans.

Acute and chronic stressors. An acute stressor refers to an event which is circumscribed in time and space. The ground-shaking of an earthquake, the touchdown of a tornado, a terrorist event involving conventional explosives, or the violence of a physical assault provide examples of acute stressors. Each has a well-defined onset and endpoint. The 1995 bombing of the Alfred P. Murrah Federal Building in Oklahoma City exemplifies an acute stressor. Forty percent of middle school and high school students in Oklahoma City knew someone who was injured and one-third knew someone who was killed (Pfefferbaum et al., 1999). A chronic stressor is characterized by ongoing exposure to continuous and unrelenting adversities, such as child maltreatment, war-related trauma, and kidnapping; or episodic, repetitive exposures as occur with periodic terrorist attacks. Children exposed to chronic stressors

Table 1.2 Primary and Secondary Stressors

Primary	Secondary
Scalding	• Hospitalization • Surgery • Debridement • Separation from parents • Loss of routines
Hurricane impact, winds, storm surge, tornadoes, floods	• Loss of shelter • School closure • Damaged worksites • Unemployment • Loss of power • Gasoline shortage • Evacuation • Loss of valued possessions • Separation from loved ones
Explosion of nuclear reactor	• Stigmatization of the area • Unemployment • Loss of community • Closing of businesses and schools • Displacement • Fear of cancer risk • Long-term health effects

may experience a gradual loss of resiliency and adaptive coping skills. Cumulative stress is associated with both immediate and long-term neurobiological changes (Cooper et al., 2007).

A distant stressor refers to a traumatic stimulus experienced from a remote and physically safe distance away from the impact zone. A distant stressor may be encountered repetitively through the media or interpersonal interactions. Television networks repeatedly broadcast images of the explosive destruction of the Space Shuttle Challenger (1986); the Oklahoma City bombing and the fiery collision of civilian airliners striking the World Trade Center towers on September 11, 2001. These traumatic stimuli were viewed time and again by children throughout the United States and around the globe. A structured interview that was conducted with children who had viewed the Challenger explosion on television found that 60 percent experienced specific fears related to death, fires, airplanes and taking risks (Terr et al., 1999). A national survey conducted 3-5 days after the September 11, 2001 attack revealed that children watched an average of three hours of television coverage of the event. One-third of the children had stress symptoms and 47 percent were concerned about their own safety (Schuster et al., 2001).

Table 1.3 Acute and Chronic Stressors

	Acute Stressors	Chronic Stressors
Life/developmental stressors	• Motor vehicle accident • Surgery • Acute illness	• Family discord • Prolonged separation from loved ones • Chronic illness
Natural disasters	• Earthquake • Hurricane • Tornado	• Pandemic
Human-generated acts of violence	• Single terrorist attack • Rape • Mugging	• War • Torture • Child maltreatment

The Stress Response

Acute Stress Response. Direct exposure to a stressor activates the acute stress response, a state of physiological "hyperarousal" frequently described as the "fight-flight-or-freeze" response. Encountering a stressor disturbs the body's biological and psychological equilibrium. The stressor is interpreted as a potentially-threatening change in the environment instantaneously activating the hypothalamic-pituitary-adrenal (HPA) axis at the base of the brain. The activated HPA axis signals the release of adrenocorticotropic hormone (ACTH) that stimulates the endocrine system and the adrenal cortex which produces cortisol. Cortisol has essential and beneficial effects in the short term (restoring depleted energy by increasing glucose availability) but detrimental effects in the long term (Perry et al., 1995; McEwen, 2004; Yehuda, 2002). This alarm reaction simultaneously stimulates the sympathetic nervous system which results in the release of epinephrine (adrenaline) from the inner part of the adrenal glands, the medulla, which prepares the individual for a "fight-or-flight" response. Epinephrine increases heart rate, blood pressure and respiration and is accompanied by a sharp spike in glucose which is released into the blood stream as an energy source, priming the body for rapid action. Simultaneously, quantities of endorphins, the body's natural painkillers, are secreted.

This adaptive response acts to restore the individual to a more optimal level of function. Regardless of whether the stressor is a minor daily hassle, a bout of the "common cold," a "fender-bender" motor vehicle accident or an overt threat to life itself, human neurobiology responds in an attempt to restore order and homeostasis. It is assumed that there is a natural impetus to recover and that with sufficient infusion of resources and the passage of time, recovery is the expected outcome to an acute stressor (Watson and Shalev, 2005).

Signs of Acute Stress

- Hyperarousal
- Pounding heart
- Trembling and shaking
- Sweating
- Shortness of breath
- Nausea
- Feeling dizzy or lightheaded
- Difficulty thinking and concentrating
- Vague bodily symptoms

Chronic Stress Response. In some instances, the traumatic situation is prolonged. Continuing exposure to chronic stressors creates long-term effects on the organism's psychological and physiological well-being. When the stress response system remains in "overdrive", high levels of epinephrine and cortisol are continuously released. Maintaining the stress response on "high alert" leads to wear and tear on organ systems and increases the risk for a number of psychobiological symptoms. These include anxiety, depressed mood, sleep and appetite disturbances, interpersonal and social problems, and diminished performance either at school or work. Bodily symptoms such as gastric ulcers, headaches, or irritable bowel syndrome may ensue. When stress and physiological "hyperarousal" continue unabated, cortisol remains elevated with possible detrimental effects on immune function and increased risk for chronic conditions such as cardiovascular disease, obesity, depression, hyperthyroidism, diabetes, and even anatomical changes in the brain (Perry et al., 1995; McEwen, 2004). In some instances, the individual's stress response is insufficient to meet the crisis. In situations of inadequate neuroendocrine response, insufficient production of adrenal stress response hormones and low levels of cortisol may elevate risks for fibromyalgia, hypothyroidism or chronic fatigue syndrome (McEwen, 2004).

Chronic Stress: Long-Term Consequences

- Sleep and appetite disturbances
- Bodily symptoms such as gastrointestinal problems, chronic pain
- Interpersonal, social and performance problems at school or work
- Trauma-specific mental disorders (acute stress disorder--ASD, post-traumatic stress disorder--PTSD)
- Anxiety and mood disorders
- Autoimmune diseases or flare-ups of these conditions (asthma, endocrine disorders)
- Cardiovascular illness

Psychobiological Responses to Chronic Stress in Children

Exposure to ongoing and repetitive traumatic experiences results in profound and reverberating effects on personality structure, psychological symptoms and developing neurobiological structures. When children remain suspended in a constant state of fearful expectation, their capacities to use cognitive, social and emotional experiences to develop solutions to problems are impaired. Moreover, continuing exposure to stress negatively impacts attachment behaviors, behavioral controls, cognition, psychobiology, self-regulation and interpersonal relationships in children. It is estimated that up to 80 percent of children who experience chronic stress (such as child victims of aggression and maltreatment by caretakers) will exhibit one or more stress-related disturbances (Kendall-Tacket et al., 1991; Hadi & Llabre, 1998; Bayer et al., 2007).

Disturbance in behavioral controls may appear as impulsivity, aggression, sleep and appetite disturbances, eating disorders, oppositional behavior, substance abuse and suicidal behaviors.

Disturbances in relationships may present as attachment disorders, social estrangement, overestimation of danger and adversity, problems with boundaries, distrust of others, a belief that intimate relations are dangerous, and avoidance of intimacy.

Negative self-attributions may occur in which the individual internalizes negative self-judgments regarding self-efficacy, competency and self-worth and a readiness for self–blame, shame, guilt, feelings of helplessness and self-loathing.

Affect dysregulation may be manifested by depression, anxiety, mood swings, emotional instability (rage, anger, and despair), suicidal thoughts or actions, impulsivity, hyperarousal, hyperactivity and substance abuse. Children may experience difficulties in identifying and describing emotions or even knowing what they feel.

Emotional/behavioral problems may include post-traumatic stress symptoms, mood and other anxiety symptoms, dissociative disorders, severe personality disturbances, and behavioral problems.

Disturbances in cognition may be appear as inattention, learning difficulties, problems with information processing, distorted social judgment and inability to interpret the intentions of others. There may be disturbances in thinking as evidenced by memory deficits, denial, repression, suppression, minimization, amnesia, and academic difficulties.

The **biological effects** of chronic stress exposure are directly related to the intensity, duration and degree of impact of stressors on bodily integrity, the stress response system and physiological systems critical for sustaining life. Abuse and neglect affect brain development. The more prolonged the maltreatment, the greater the residual effects. Exposure to intense acute and chronic stressors during the developmental years has enduring neurobiological effects on the stress response, neurotransmitter systems and anatomical structures. Children who have been physically and sexually abused have decreased brain volumes (decreased size of the cerebrum and the corpus callosum) and poor regulation of the stress response (DeBellis et al., 1999a,b).

The Traumatic Event

A **traumatic event** occurs when an individual experiences, witnesses, or is confronted with an event that involves death, serious injury, or threats to the physical integrity of the self or others (APA, 1994). Exposure to trauma may occur from direct physical impact, visual exposure, media presentation, or through interpersonal relationships with disaster survivors. Experiencing multiple types of trauma exposure increases the risk of psychological consequences.

The essence of the traumatic situation is embodied in feelings of helplessness and fears of imminent death (Shaw, 1987). Trauma may lead to a perceived sense that life has lost its intrinsic meaning and predictability and may never be the same again. The individual grapples with the need to accept and assimilate what has happened and to ultimately find new meaning and purpose (Doctors Without Borders, 2005). The adolescent may be left with a sense of a "foreshortened future" and take flight into pleasure-seeking or risk-taking activities.

Trauma invariably impacts not only the individual, but also the family and social system within which the individual lives. The impact of trauma in children is modulated by the fact that the child has limited life experience. The child is still developing cognitively and emotionally and may be struggling with such issues as separation, individuation, and identity formation. Children typically exhibit immature adaptive and coping strategies. When exposed to trauma, children rarely describe such emotions as fear and helplessness; rather, they may respond with disorganized or agitated behavior.

The Traumatic Event

A traumatic event is stated to have occurred when the person experiences, witnesses, or is confronted with an event that involves actual or threatened death or serious injury, or a threat to the physical integrity of the self or others often associated with fear, helplessness, or terror. Children rarely will describe such emotions and may respond with disorganized or agitated behavior.

Source: American Psychiatric Association, 1994

The Acute Traumatic Moment

The **acute traumatic moment** is defined as the sudden, conscious awareness of vulnerability in the presence of imminent physical injury or death. For children it is often the sudden awareness that parents are unable to protect and provide for them in their hour of need that ushers in and exacerbates the traumatic moment. The illusion of safety is shattered. The traumatic moment may be associated with feelings of helplessness and anxiety (Shaw, 1987).

A distinguishing feature of the traumatic moment is the central role of anxiety and its management. Most commonly, the brief traumatic moment, with its experience of anxiety and helplessness, is followed by rapid remobilization and reintegration of developmentally-appropriate coping and adaptive strategies. The child who is able to successfully adapt will restore normal developmental progression with age-appropriate self-direction, academic performance, and peer and family relations. In some instances, distress persists and there is a failure of reparative defenses leading to a sustained traumatic experience. This may precipitate various degrees of regression with loss of developmental achievements and psychosocial gains as well as various symptoms of somatic ills, anxiety, mood and behavioral disturbances (Shaw, 2000).

Traumatic Reminders

In the aftermath of an acute trauma, the survivor may experience "flashbacks", in which they vividly relive the traumatic moment over and over again. "Flashbacks" are frequently triggered by "**traumatic reminders**", external or internal cues that suddenly make the individual feel as if the traumatic event was happening again. For example, sudden exposure to strong winds, torrential rains, thunder and lightning may bring back all the emotions, fears, and cognitions associated with living through a hurricane. A child who was once painfully injured in a bicycle accident may re-experience all the emotions, ideations and physical sensations of that event when exposed to the cue of seeing another child's mangled bicycle.

Summary

Children and adolescents are exposed to various types of stress and traumatic events during their developmental years. The individual response to stress is shaped both by the reality of the impact of the fateful event and by one's subjective appraisal. How you define a situation determines your emotional response. Stressors may be acute or chronic. A traumatic event occurs when an individual experiences a situation in which there is a perceived or real threat of bodily injury or death. The acute traumatic moment for the child involves a sudden awareness of vulnerability in the presence of probable physical harm or death. Traumatic reminders refer to those events in the aftermath of traumatic exposure that result in the child or adolescent reliving and re-experiencing the trauma as if it was truly recurring at that moment.

CH 2

Natural and Human-Generated Disasters

Chapter 2

Natural and Human-Generated Disasters

On successful completion of this chapter you should be able to:

1) Define the concept of disaster
2) Describe the phases of the disaster life cycle
3) Describe the time-phased community response to disaster
4) Compare and contrast natural and human-generated disasters in terms of forces of harm and stressors
5) Understand the role of traumatic reminders

Key Concepts

- A disaster is an encounter between forces of harm and a human population in harm's way, influenced by the ecological context, in which demands exceed the coping capacity of the disaster-affected community.
- The disaster life cycle consists of pre-impact, impact and post-impact phases.
- Community response to disaster proceeds through a predictable sequence of stages.
- Natural and human-generated disasters differ in their psychological effects.
- Each type of disaster is associated with a unique constellation of stressors.

Source: NOAA

Introduction

"The stars are against us," is the literal interpretation of the melding of two Greek roots, "dis" and "astrum" to create "disaster". The World Health Organization (WHO) describes disaster as a severe ecological and psychosocial disruption which greatly exceeds the coping capacity of the altered community (WHO, 1992). A parallel but expanded definition is: A disaster is characterized as an encounter between forces of harm and a human population in harm's way, influenced by the ecological context, in which the demands of the situation exceed the coping capacity of the affected population, (Shultz, et al. 2006). The common denominator in these definitions is that demand exceeds coping capacity, thus generating massive harm and destruction, compounded with feelings of powerlessness, and helplessness.

Definition: Disaster

A disaster is characterized as an encounter between forces of harm and a human population in harm's way, influenced by the ecological context, in which the demands of the situation exceed the coping capacity of the affected population

Source: Shultz, et al. 2006

The nature of the disaster determines the level of response required from the affected community and from sources beyond the impact zone. Disasters may be categorized based on the level of response required to meet the demands. For example, Waeckerle (1991) distinguished disasters requiring only local response assets (Level I), from those requiring regional response (Level II) or federal response (Level III). Hick (2005) has distinguished six "tiers" of response for health care responders: healthcare facility (Tier 1), healthcare coalition (Tier 2), county-level response (Tier 3), intrastate region (Tier 4), state/interstate response (Tier 5) and federal response (Tier 6).

Extreme events may also be classified in relation to the balance between demand and community capacity to meet the demand (Table 2.1).

Table 2.1 Extreme Event Classification	
Crisis	Capacity exceeds demand and local assets capably handle the demand
Emergency	Capacity is challenged by demand, but local assets are able to manage the demand
Disaster	Demand exceeds capacity, necessitating a call for outside assistance
Catastrophe	Demand overwhelms and destroys local capacity, creating near-total dependence on outside response

Source: Quarantelli, 2006; Shultz et al. 2007

*Burundi: refugee camp 2002 © EC/ECHO/Yves Horent
Available at http://ec.europa.eu/echo*

Catastrophe Example: Hurricane Katrina

On occasion, a disaster is so extreme that demand not only overwhelms capacity, but in fact, local response capabilities are destroyed. The term "catastrophe" is reserved for such capacity-obliterating events (Quarantelli, 2006). Hurricane Katrina's devastation of New Orleans graphically depicts such a catastrophe. At 6:10 AM, August 28, 2005, a Category 3 hurricane made landfall just east of New Orleans (population: 484,674) and on that day, two major levees were breached. By the morning of August 30, 80 percent of New Orleans was under water, stranding 50,000-100,000 citizens, many clinging to rooftops. Approximately 25,000 people sought shelter in the New Orleans Superdome. City and regional support services were submerged in flood waters and inoperable. Food, water, electrical power, emergency and life-supporting services were unavailable. Community infrastructure was destroyed, looting and crime were widespread, and political and ethnic fissures quickly surfaced with allegations of blame and racism. Reflecting on Katrina, Quarantelli (2006) described the elements that make a catastrophe categorically distinct from a disaster: 1) emergency organizations and operational bases are so severely strained that they become unresponsive; 2) city and local officials are unable to perform their leadership roles; 3) community services are destroyed and assistance from the affected community is not available; 4) local mass media ceases to function so the disaster is described by news sources from afar; and 5) conflict surfaces along the fault lines of race, class, and ethnicity.

Types of Disasters

Psychological responses resonate with the forces of harm inherent within each disaster. The universe of disasters is generally divided into two broad categories, natural disasters and human-generated disasters. Psychological outcomes in children and adults are shaped by the distinguishing features of each category of disaster, as well as the unique characteristics of each specific event (Galea and Resnick, 2005). Exposure to natural disasters is part of the life experience of most individuals, and such events tend to be somewhat familiar and predictable although generally not preventable. In contrast, direct exposure to human-generated acts of violence tends to be outside common experience, unfamiliar, unanticipated, and unpredictable (IOM, 2003). Purposeful infliction of harm characterizes both interpersonal aggression (Breslau et al., 1998) and large-scale mass violence. The feature distinguishing acts of mass violence, including terrorism, is "malicious human intent". Persons exposed to such intentional acts are at elevated risk for severe psychological impairment compared with individuals who are impacted by natural disasters or non-intentional human-generated events (Norris et al., 2002).

Natural disasters are often described as "acts of nature" and subcategorized as 1) weather-related disasters (hurricanes, tornadoes, floods), 2) geophysical disasters (earthquakes, volcanoes, and tsunamis), 3) droughts

and wildfires, and 4) pandemic diseases (CRED, 2006). **Human-generated disasters** include unintentional transportation, industrial, and other miscellaneous accidents; ecological/environmental destruction; and intentional acts of violence such as war, civil strife, ethnic violence and terrorism. Failures of technology resulting in disaster are rarely intentional, although poor judgment and negligence may be relevant human factors in determining the degree of psychological impact.

Complex emergencies have been defined as "relatively acute situations affecting large civilian populations, usually involving a continuation of war or civil strife, food shortages and population displacement resulting in significant excess morbidity" (Toole, 1990), According to the World Health Organization and United Nations, a complex emergency is "a humanitarian crisis in a country, region or society where there is considerable breakdown of authority resulting from internal or external conflict which requires an international response that goes beyond the mandate or capacity of any single agency. Complex emergencies are typically characterized by: excessive violence and loss of life; massive displacements of people; widespread damage to societies and economies; the need for large-scale, multifaceted humanitarian assistance; the hindrance or prevention of humanitarian assistance by political and military constraints, and considerable security risks for humanitarian relief workers in some areas," (UNDP, 2004).

Disaster Classification

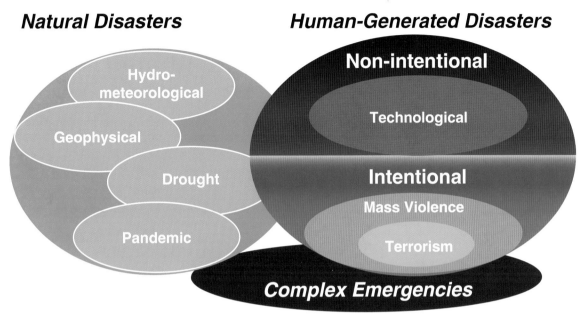

Natural Disasters   **Human-Generated Disasters**

- Hydro-meteorological
- Geophysical
- Drought
- Pandemic

Non-intentional
- Technological

Intentional
- Mass Violence
- Terrorism

Complex Emergencies

Sources: Shultz et al. 2007

Natural Disasters

Hydrometeorological Disasters (Weather-related)

- **Floods and Related Disasters**
  - Floods
  - Landslides/mudslides
  - Avalanches
- **Windstorms**
  - Tropical cyclones (hurricanes, cyclones, typhoons, tropical storms)
  - Tornadoes
  - Storms (thunderstorms, winter storms)

Geophysical Disasters

- Earthquakes
- Volcanic eruptions
- Tsunamis

Droughts and Related Disasters

- Extreme temperatures
- Wildfires
- Droughts
- Insect infestation

Pandemic Diseases

Human-Generated Disasters

Non-Intentional/Technological

- Industrial accidents
- Transportation accidents
- Ecological/environmental destruction
- Miscellaneous accidents

Intentional

- Declared war
- Civil strife
- Ethnic conflict
- Violent mass gatherings and demonstrations
- Terrorism

Complex Emergencies

Situations characterized by:
- Extensive violence and loss of life; massive displacements of people; widespread damage to societies and economies
- Need for large-scale, multi-faceted humanitarian assistance
- Hindrance or prevention of humanitarian assistance by political and military constraints

Source: Shultz et al. 2007

Disaster Life Cycle

The pre-impact phase includes both the inter-disaster period as well as the warning period. The pre-impact phase is characterized by disaster planning and preparatory procedures. When conditions warrant or a detectable threat has been identified, warnings are issued to alert the public that a disaster is probable or imminent. Tornado, hurricane or tsunami warnings are issued in the areas where a strike is most likely. Credible intelligence regarding a terrorist threat may prompt the federal government to raise the alert level and notify the public of actions to take.

During the impact phase, citizens encounter the full impact of the disaster hazards, the "forces of harm." This phase is characterized by maximum likelihood of bodily injury and death, physical destruction and widespread community disruption. Individuals in harm's way fear for their lives as they witness gruesome scenes of devastation or extreme harm to others. Some survivors will sustain injury. Others will lose a loved one, and for children, this may be a parent or caregiver.

Confronted by overwhelming forces during disaster impact, many children and adults will experience helplessness and passivity. Some individuals will respond with heroic efforts to save self, family, others and the community. Individuals frequently come together with a new sense of group cohesiveness and solidarity in an effort to protect the community and to mobilize resources for recovery. In the immediate aftermath, a profound sense of relief and triumph often emerges for those individuals who have escaped injury and death and are able to reunite with loved ones who have also survived.

Following impact, survivors may enter a prolonged period of mounting adversity. In this post-impact phase an

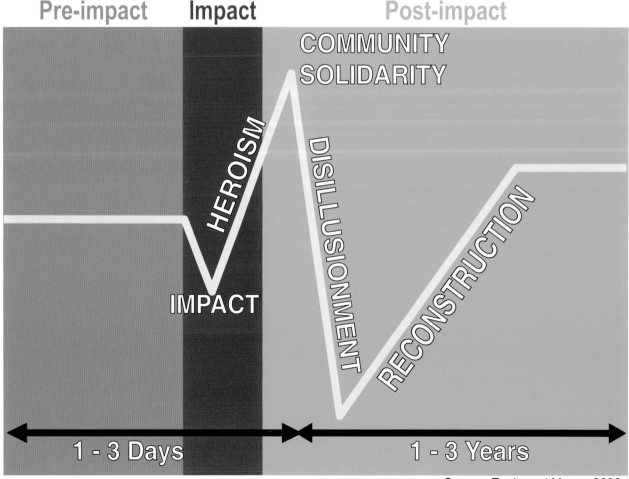

Source: Zunin and Myers, 2000

escalating sense of disillusionment may emerge as people become aware of the enormity of the tasks necessary to achieve full recovery. Survivors take stock of the inventory of compounding stressors such as loss of home and shelter, closure of schools, unemployment, economic losses, damage to community infrastructure, loss of social supports and pervasive psychological distress and impairment. Reconstruction is tangled in bureaucracy and requires negotiating with insurance adjusters; code inspectors; and local, state and national authorities for help and financial assistance. It soon becomes apparent to survivors that recovery is a process that takes years.

Acts of terrorism are intentional, human-generated events that usually occur without warning. However, from the moment of impact forward, the community response follows a similar trajectory to that observed for natural disasters (Ahearn and Cohen, 1985). Following the "heroic phase", in which individuals often exhibit courageous and heroic behaviors and experience relief associated with their survival, there is often a coming together with a sense of national resolve and a heightened sense of patriotism, as community, state or national support systems facilitate recovery. This phase may last from weeks to several months. After September 11, 2001, there was a sense of national solidarity coupled with a sense of optimism that America would prevail against the terrorists. This outpouring of communal feelings and enhanced sense of revitalization has been described as a "stage of euphoria", "post-disaster utopia", or an "altruistic community" as the "communal body is not only intact but mobilizes its resources to dress the wound" (Erikson, 1976). Individuals bind their anxiety by immersing themselves in a group process in which they submerge their personal vulnerabilities in the group, which is viewed as all-powerful and protective. Subsequently, however, there is often a phase in which there is increasing awareness of uncertainty, fear of other attacks, emerging disappointments and a readiness to externalize blame on political leaders and government for not doing enough to protect the community. Eventually there is a greater readiness to accept reality, to realistically appraise risk and danger and to proactively begin to work together to protect the community.

Natural Disasters

Natural disasters are common; on average, one natural disaster is reported each day to the international disaster registry (Shultz et al., 2007). A community-based population survey of young adults found that 13 percent had been exposed to a natural disaster during their lifetimes (Breslau et al., 1991). Corroborating this finding, a longitudinal study of children in western North Carolina indicated that 11 percent had been exposed to a natural disaster before 16 years of age (Copeland et al., 2007).

The level of psychiatric risk varies with the specific nature of the disaster, the degree of personal exposure, the extent of physical destruction and community disruption, and the range of stressful adversities in the aftermath.

Source: NOAA

Hurricanes

A hurricane is a tropical cyclone, typically hundreds of miles in diameter, characterized by powerful winds, torrential rains, and storm surge, forces of harm that may also produce inland flooding, mudslides and tornadoes. The most intense cyclonic winds are found in the "eyewall", rotating ferociously around the perimeter of the calm "eye" of the storm. Tropical cyclones form in seven "hurricane basins" distributed along the midsection of the globe, both north and south of the equator. Tropical cyclones occurring in the Atlantic and Eastern Pacific Basins are termed "hurricanes." The number of hurricanes that form each year varies by basin and is affected by many factors including ocean temperatures and global weather systems. In the United States, the official hurricane season extends from

June 1 to November 30 with a sharp peak in August and September. Hurricane frequency rises and falls over 30 to 50 year cycles with the decade of the 2000's representing a period of increased frequency. It is anticipated that the current active period for Atlantic Basin hurricanes will continue for another 15 to 20 years (Klotzbach & Gray, 2005).

Hurricanes are identified and tracked as they move across the ocean waters, often maintaining hurricane strength for hundreds of miles, and for periods of days to weeks. Some storms stay over the open ocean, never affecting island or coastal inhabitants. Some hurricanes make multiple landfalls (Hurricane Ivan devastated Grenada before hammering the panhandle of Florida in 2004) or track parallel to coastlines, deluging land areas beneath the spiraling canopy of thunderstorms (Hurricane Mitch, 1998, stayed over warm Caribbean waters, close to Honduras and Nicaragua as incessant rains triggered deadly mudslides).

The National Hurricane Center issues a hurricane watch for coastal areas where there is potential for landfall within 24 to 36 hours. A hurricane warning is issued within 24 hours of possible strike. Long warning periods provide the opportunity for families to prepare and to evacuate if necessary.

Pre-impact hurricane stressors. Hurricane warnings provide advance notice to citizens, giving them time to protect property, shutter windows, safeguard family members and move from harm's way by evacuating or relocating to shelters. Nevertheless, hurricane warnings provoke anticipatory anxiety and emotional distress given the uncertainty as to when and where the hurricane will make landfall. Often a contagion of fear and anxiety spreads as families and the community prepare for the storm. Community members may frantically shop for food, water, flashlights, batteries, generators, and materials such as shutters and plywood for boarding up windows. Long lines may form as cars queue up for gasoline in preparation for evacuation. Acute shortages of supplies commonly occur. Families struggle to consolidate plans to be together in one safe place or to evacuate. Decisions must be made about sheltering in place or selecting

essential items for each family member if rapid evacuation is necessary.

Impact and post-impact hurricane stressors. Often long before the "eye" of the hurricane makes landfall, communication networks may be disrupted. Loss of electrical power may compromise food and water supplies. Threats of physical injury and fears for one's life are common as the powerful storm propels wind-driven projectiles, shatters windows, destroys roofs, and creates massive physical destruction over large areas. Tropical storm and hurricane force winds may continue for many hours. Torrential rains, tornadoes, and inland flooding create additional hazards. During impact, children may witness anxiety and fear in their parents and caretakers, undermining their own sense of confidence. Eighty-five percent of children who directly experienced the impact of Hurricane Andrew manifested moderate to severe levels of posttraumatic stress symptoms with a marked increase in disruptive behaviors in school immediately after the hurricane (Shaw et al., 1995). After the storm, children may be exposed to closed or damaged schools and destruction of community landmarks. Personal memorabilia and favorite toys may be lost. Children may experience the horror of seeing severely-injured survivors or even dead bodies.

Hurricane Katrina was catastrophically devastating. The federally-declared disaster area spanned 90,000 square miles. There were 1,600 confirmed deaths and hundreds remained missing months after the storm (Kessler et al., 2006). More than 100,000 residents of New Orleans, primarily of minority race and ethnicity, were unable to evacuate from the city (Cordasco et al., 2007). The baseline rate of any mental illness doubled from 15 to 30 percent post-Katrina (Kessler et al., 2006).

Traumatic reminders. Common traumatic reminders are the annual onset of hurricane season, hurricane warnings, the sudden appearance of towering dark clouds, bolts of lightening, torrential rains, gusting winds, and hurricane preparedness activities.

Earthquakes

In contrast to hurricanes, earthquakes occur suddenly and unexpectedly. Annually, approximately 70 earthquakes impact human populations, but few cause extreme damage, destruction, injury, and death. Earthquakes are caused by powerful seismic forces occurring along the boundaries of the earth's tectonic plates. The trembling of the earth may create shockwaves that move sideways, or up and down, and may extend over very large surface areas. Earthquakes last from a few seconds to several minutes, and are accompanied by a low-pitched rumbling noise that resembles the sound of a freight train.

Earthquake strength is measured by two methods. The Richter scale measures the amount of energy released by the earthquake. The surface strength of an earthquake

Earthquakes originating beneath the ocean's floor may generate a tsunami (Japanese: "tsu"-harbor and "nami"-wave), enormous waves moving outward from the epicenter with extraordinary velocity and propulsion. The Great Sumatra-Andaman Earthquake of December 26, 2004 produced the Indian Ocean Tsunami resulting in 283,000 deaths along 10,000s of miles of coastline in such nations as Indonesia, India, Sri Lanka, and Thailand. This tsunami instantly created an unprecedented humanitarian crisis characterized by mass bereavement and displacement of more than one million persons (Lay et al., 2005). A study of 325 tsunami-exposed adolescents in Sri Lanka found that mediators of mental health included the intensity of traumatic exposure, displacement from home, loss of social and family supports, and maternal depression (Wickrama & Kaspar, 2007). A positive mother-child relationship was

Source: FEMA Photo Library

Source: Tsunami in Asia: India - Tamil Nadu
2005 © EC/ECHO South Asia Office

varies from imperceptible to extreme. The Modified Mercalli scale measures the amount of damage and destruction caused by the earthquake, a preferred metric for estimating human impact.

Earthquakes may produce extensive damage with destruction of government and commercial buildings, schools, homes, bridges, dams and highways. Severed gas mains and downed power lines may ignite fires, while disruption of water supplies and buckled roadways may interfere with the fire-fighting response. Water supplies may become cross-contaminated with broken sewage lines, increasing the risk for infectious disease. Earthquake aftershocks commonly occur for days to months afterward, sometimes causing more damage and injury than the original quake.

a protective factor that diminished the rate and severity of depressive and posttraumatic stress symptoms in the adolescents.

Pre-impact earthquake stressors. The reality that earthquakes occur rarely and unpredictably may breed complacency and a tendency for persons to minimize risk despite living in seismically-active areas. Families can mitigate earthquake risk by locating away from tectonic plate boundary zones and other areas of extreme earthquake risk. Other options include selecting housing constructed to minimize the destructive potential of earthquakes and disaster-proofing older housing units. Involving the family in the creation of an all-hazards family disaster plan that includes periodic earthquake drills is a prudent strategy.

Impact and post-impact earthquake stressors. The sudden, unexpected, and violent experience of ground-shaking during an earthquake may provoke feelings of helplessness, terror and fear. The earth's apparent stability is instantaneously transformed into a landscape of quaking destruction. Individuals and families may be injured and trapped in collapsed structures when homes, schools, shopping centers and highways succumb to the liquefaction of the earth. Children may become separated from parents and family members with hours passing before knowing whether their loved ones are safe. Children may witness scenes of severe injury, entrapment, crushed bodies and brutal death. Widespread harm and ongoing danger may be compounded by the abrupt loss of community infrastructure, power and other utilities, communications systems, and health care services. Obtaining such basic necessities as food and water may become an acute challenge.

For children exposed to the Northridge earthquake in Los Angeles (1994), risk for posttraumatic stress symptoms was related to the degree of life threat, the frequency of exposure to traumatic reminders such as aftershocks, the extent of physical damage to their dwelling and their subjective appraisal of their own actions during the earthquake. (Pynoos et al., 1998; 1993). Children exposed to the catastrophic earthquake in Armenia (1988) displayed increased rates of PTSD and adolescents exhibited altered neurohormonal stress responses five years after exposure (Pynoos et al., 1998). A study of 2,037 children, ages 9-17 years, who were exposed to the Athens earthquake in 1999, found that PTSD rates were highest for those who were directly impacted and those with the highest degree

of perceived threat (Giannopoulou et al., 2006). PTSD rates were higher for younger children and for girls.

Traumatic reminders. Sudden and repetitive aftershocks intensify anxiety and fear responses. Traumatic reminders may include jagged cracks in walls and masonry, rumbling noises, unrepaired and heavily damaged buildings, piles of rubble, strong odors of fire or decay, and broadcast news reports about the earthquake.

Tornadoes

A tornado is a violently rotating column of air, in contact with the ground, beneath a cumuliform cloud, that is typically visible as a funnel cloud (Glickman, 2000). The central United States experiences the highest frequency of tornadoes on Earth. Tornadoes may be up to two miles in width at the base and wind speeds, graded on the Fujita scale, may exceed 200 miles per hour. Tornadoes most commonly occur in the spring and summer, touching down in erratic, jagged and unpredictable paths.

Devastation is immediate and sporadically extreme; buildings may be explosively destroyed in a matter of seconds. In the United States, approximately 800 tornadoes form during a typical year, collectively causing about 1,500 injuries and 80 deaths.

Pre-impact tornado stressors. Advances in weather prediction and forecasting have reduced tornado-related injuries and fatalities. Tornado "watch boxes" are posted for areas where climatic conditions are conducive for tornado formation. Nevertheless, the warning period for active tornadoes is brief under the best circumstances,

Chapter 2

and nonexistent for many areas. When a tornado warning is issued, families must take shelter immediately.

Impact and post-impact tornado stressors. Tornadoes do not typically create widespread destruction on the scale of hurricane damage. Damage patterns tend to be spotty and inconsistent with areas of complete devastation interspersed with areas that are untouched. Intense tornadoes produce extreme pressure gradients that may shatter buildings in the path of destruction. Alternatively, entire structures such as houses, barns, and silos have been lofted from their foundations and hurled airborne for great distances. Early in 2007, a devastating, 1.7-mile-wide tornado destroyed 95 percent of all dwellings and structures in Greensburg, Kansas.

Children may see collapsed buildings, destroyed barns and dead farm animals and experience the horror of seeing severely injured people or dead bodies. The

Source: FEMA Photo Library

sudden onset and violence of a tornado, and the random pattern of destruction, often leads children to question, why me? Bloch et al. (1956) studied children impacted by a tornado that had destroyed a movie theatre in Vicksburg, Mississippi and found that one-third demonstrated significant psychological impairment. Factors mediating severity of psychological distress were proximity to the theater, being injured, knowing somebody who was injured or killed and parental psychological response.

Traumatic reminders. Traumatic reminders include the beginning of the tornado season, tornado watches and warnings, the sound of the tornado siren, the appearance

of menacing cloud formations (especially when thick cloud banks take on a distinctive pea-green coloration). Other reminders are those that invoke memories of the brutality of the storm such as thunder, lightning, torrential rains, and powerful wind gusts.

Wildfires

The onset of wildfires is as unpredictable as a lightning strike or the careless flick of a burning ember. Some wildfires are intentionally ignited as an act of arson. Wildfires can spread quickly, destroying large acreages of woodlands and wildlife, as well as residential areas, businesses and schools. Wildfires are a growing natural hazard in most regions of the United States, posing a threat to life and property, particularly where native ecosystems meet developed areas. The secondary effects of wildfires, including erosion, landslides, introduction of invasive species, and changes in water quality, are often more disastrous than the fire itself.

Pre-impact wildfire stressors. Wildfires occur suddenly and unexpectedly. No formal warning systems exist. The path, speed, and damage potential of a wildfire are highly variable depending upon shifting wind patterns, rainfall and climate conditions, terrain, availability and density of dry tinder and fuel, human settlement patterns and local fire-fighting capabilities and resources for combating wildfires.

Source: FEMA Photo Library

Impact and post-impact wildfire stressors. The rapid and unrelenting approach of a firestorm that threatens to consume the family home and surrounding neighborhood, provokes fear and distress for those in harm's way. An encounter with fire and conflagration carries a particularly powerful threat of excruciating pain and horrific harm for self and loved ones. Neighborhoods and communities may be called upon to evacuate on short notice, forcing people to make important decisions in minutes such as to try to save the home or to evacuate (where to go?, when to leave?, what to bring?). McFarlane et al. (1987), studying the effects of a bush fire on 808 children in Australia, ages 5-12 years, found significant and sustained levels of psychological stress at 8 and 26 months after traumatic exposure.

Traumatic reminders. The sound of crackling fire or the smell of smoke may trigger a sudden reliving and re-experiencing of the encounter with a wildfire. Other reminders may be those of the firefighting response such as a siren wailing, the high-speed approach of a fire truck, the sound of low-flying aircraft, or media accounts of wildfires or house fires.

Source: FEMA Photo Library

Pandemics

Infectious disease is the leading cause of death worldwide and remains a prominent cause of death in the United States and the developed world. Human existence has been punctuated by epidemics of infectious diseases that have shaped and transformed history. The plague of Athens (400 B.C.) contributed to the defeat of the Athenians by Sparta in the Peloponnesian War. In the middle of the 14th century, one-third of the population in Europe died from the Black Death (bubonic plague). The Spanish Influenza epidemic of 1918/1919 killed between 50 and 100 million persons worldwide. The pandemic of HIV/AIDS, first recognized in the 1980s, evolved to become the second

leading cause of disability and the fourth leading cause of mortality worldwide by the end of the Twentieth Century.

The predominant global infectious disease threat of the early 2000s is the prospect of pandemic H5N1 influenza, or "avian flu". The first human case was diagnosed in 1997. The virus has been associated with high lethality and complete absence of human immunity. No vaccine is currently available (Leavitt, 2006). Efficient human-to-human transmission may occur with devastating consequences as the virus progressively mutates. H5N1 appears capable of provoking an exaggerated immune response with death occurring rapidly in persons across a wide age span, including many adolescents and young adults in robust health. One study revealed that the pathology of H5N1 influenza mimics many of the salient characteristics of the 1918/1919 pandemic strain. The Secretary of Health and Human Services in the United

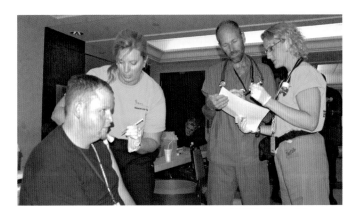

Source: FEMA Photo Library

States has noted that we are in a race with a fast moving virulent virus that can lead to a world-wide pandemic.

Once human-to-human transmission is established, H5N1 would likely circumnavigate the globe in several weeks to months. The initial wave is likely to be followed by subsequent, potentially more lethal waves of infection. Early detection is vital to warn the population to take measures to diminish the spread of the disease. Steps are being taken to develop a laboratory diagnostic test that will result in being able to diagnose the presence of the virus within a matter of a few hours. While no vaccine for the pandemic strain of H5N1 will be immediately available, an effort is underway to develop cell-based vaccine production to supplant older, slower, egg-based technologies. A strategic national stockpile of antiviral agents such as Tamiflu and Relenza is being accumulated. It is generally agreed that the most effective prevention strategies will be to 1) maintain interpersonal distance ("social distancing"), 2) practice hand-washing hygiene and cough etiquette, 3) judiciously wear masks and gowns during the pandemic phase (WHO, 2006).

Pre-impact pandemic stressors. Human behavior during this period is a critical factor. Public education regarding pandemic flu should begin during early phases of the pandemic alert period. Once the pandemic is underway, warning periods will be reduced to days or weeks. The specific nature of the infectious agent, including its capability to infect (infectivity), cause clinical disease (pathogenicity), and kill its victims (virulence) will interplay with the population's ability to engage in preventive behaviors and to receive vaccines, antiviral medications, and medical treatment. The potential exists for global hardship, beginning even prior to the arrival of the pandemic, as citizens begin to hoard food and essentials for the weeks of social distancing, creating acute shortages. Because the pandemic will sweep the globe, no areas will be spared. The inability to restock food and essential supplies may lead to widespread scarcity and possible outbreaks of violence.

Impact and post-impact pandemic stressors. Policy designed to prevent the spread of influenza must be implemented. Since person-to-person spread is the predominant mode of transmission of influenza virus, public health officials have suggested the employment of social distancing with specific targeting of children and adolescents. This approach requires the closing of schools which will represent a social stressor for children who are suddenly deprived of school-based peer relations and normal daily routines. If public health measures, including movement restrictions, are put into force, public reactions of anxiety, anger and belligerence related to quarantine, social distancing, and separation will likely proliferate. Development of effective risk communications designed to educate the public regarding disease risks and preventive efforts may serve as a buffer against fear escalating to panic. Glass et al. (2006) reviewed public

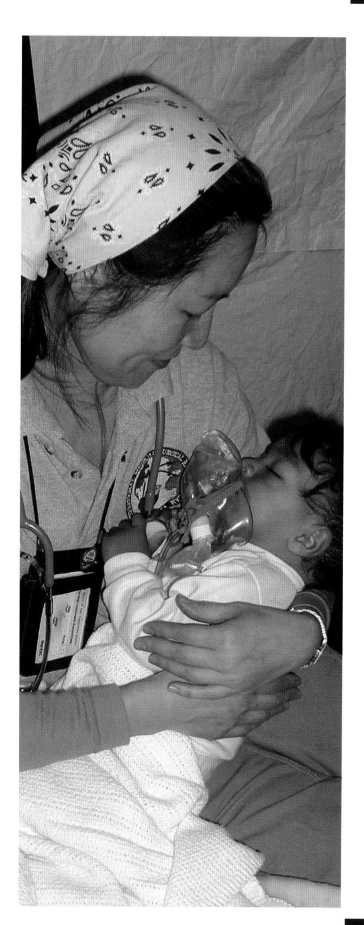

health strategies implemented during the 1957-58 Asian flu epidemic and found that closing schools and keeping children at home reduced the attack rate by over 90 percent. School closure may be a critical and effective strategy to minimize contagion.

As the pandemic moves through an area, uncertainty regarding .possible exposure to the H5N1 virus will increase anxiety among families and their children. Individuals will be vulnerable to misinformation or contradictory and exaggerated news reports. If the media and public risk communications are not managed properly, the risk for

Source: FEMA Photo Library

chaos and the likelihood of a surge of fearful citizens on medical care facilities will be heightened. Individuals will be upset, demoralized and likely to misattribute somatic symptoms to disease.

When the pandemic is at hand, large numbers of citizens will become ill and many others will be tending to loved ones in the grotesque throes of disease. Children and adolescents may directly witness the physical incapacitation and death of their primary caretakers, family members and closest friends. The contagion of anxiety, fear and overwhelming feelings of helplessness will extend across many family members as they struggle to access medical care and face an uncertain fate.

Pandemic Influenza: Special Considerations for Children

The Canadian Paediatric Society (2006) has identified the following "special considerations" regarding the health care needs of children during pandemic influenza:

- Since health care delivery for young children requires a higher staff-to-patient ratio than for adults, anticipated staff shortages during a pandemic may acutely impact the quality and availability of child health care.
- Parents and caregivers are integral to their children's care at home and while hospitalized. However, many parents will become ill or die from influenza and be unavailable to provide life-sustaining care to children.
- Schools may be closed and may be converted for use as alternative medical treatment sites. This will deprive children of school-based social support and disrupt routines. Meanwhile, health care professionals with young families will face the challenge of having their own children at home during work hours.
- Dosages and schedules for vaccines and antiviral medications will need to be adjusted for use with children.

Traumatic reminders. Traumatic reminders will include media stories about epidemic diseases, the annual arrival of (non-pandemic) influenza season, rapid spread of other familiar or newly-emergent infectious diseases, and caring for a seriously ill relative or loved one.

Human-Generated Disasters

Terrorism

Terrorism is the unlawful use, or threat of use, of force or violence against individuals or property, governments or societies, often to achieve political, religious, or ideological objectives (U.S. Department of Defense, 1990). Terrorists typically strike suddenly and unexpectedly, sometimes orchestrating a simultaneous attack on multiple targets such as the Attack on America, September 11, 2001, or a series of repeated events such as suicide bombings in Israel or the killings by the "DC Sniper."

The increasing imbalance of power between the "haves" and "have-nots" of the world has tempted those less technologically sophisticated to use acts of terror to redress the perceived imbalance. The armamentarium of weapons available to terrorists is increasing in variety, sophistication, lethality, accessibility, and ease of use. As the destructive potential of terrorist actions increases, so too does the likelihood that small groups of terrorists may achieve disproportionate power to overthrow rivals.

"Terrorism is intended to provoke collective fear and uncertainty" (IOM, 2003). This fear often spreads rapidly like concentric circles from a rock thrown into a pond affecting those directly impacted and extending out to other family members and the community at large. Terrorist attacks, or the threat of attack, may provoke severe psychological consequences associated with a perceived lack of control and an accompanying sense of helplessness. Terrorism has the capacity to erode the sense of community and national security; damage morale, social solidarity and cohesion; and divide the community along racial, ethnic, economic and religious fault-lines.

Types of Terrorist Events

Nuclear detonation: The Department of Homeland Security has created a series of National Planning Scenarios, a litany of highly-challenging disaster prototypes. Most destructive on the list is the detonation of a 10-kiloton nuclear device in an American metropolitan area. If this scenario were to become a reality, immediate and unprecedented physical destruction, widespread and

Source: FEMA Photo Library

life-threatening contamination, immediate death of tens of thousands of citizens due to initial blast injuries, and agonizing death over weeks to months among persons exposed to lethal doses of radiation would ensue. First responders would be exposed to high doses of radiation. Large numbers of persons would sustain painful but non-fatal blast injuries including burns, blistering, and possible blindness related to visual exposure. Radioactive contamination would occur due to either external exposure from the blast and fallout, or internal exposure from ingestion of contaminated food and water.

Psychological impact would be extreme due to direct observation of the event for those near the scene and from media presentation of the aftermath of detonation. The invisible nature of the radiation threat would lead to feelings of uncertainty, fear, anxiety and desperate attempts to access health care facilities. Fears would extend to uncertainty about long-term health effects such as cancer.

Massive population displacement, enforced evacuation, and relocation would be powerful realities as large geographic expanses are rendered uninhabitable in the aftermath of a nuclear detonation. These areas would experience destruction of the social fabric of the community, loss of infrastructure, and lifelong stigmatization. All facilities and services, including schools, business, and faith-based organizations would cease to function. The concept of post-disaster restoration and reconstruction would be fundamentally altered by the inability of disaster survivors to repopulate their communities.

Chemical attack: The Department of Homeland Security has described a variety of potential scenarios around the theme of chemical attack. These include attacks using nerve agents, blister agents, and chlorine gas. Historically, when chemical attacks and hazardous materials spills have occurred, large numbers of persons in the vicinity have experienced fear regarding possible exposure. The invisible nature of the threat creates uncertainty regarding the boundaries of exposure; many more persons seek screening than are actually at risk. Chemical attacks typically involve release of aerosolized, heavier-than-air agents (for example, sarin, chlorine,

anthrax) that accumulate close to the ground, creating amplified risks for smaller children. Children are thought to be more vulnerable to radioactive gas exposure and subsequent cancer risk because of their high respiratory rate (Markenson & Reynolds, 2006).

An additional stressor is the lack of information regarding risks and strategies for self-protection. Fear may provoke rapid, mass exodus from the area of perceived danger, leading to the possibility of injury as large numbers flee. When escape routes are perceived to be limited and entrapment is feared, the potential for mass panic is heightened. Large-scale surges on health care facilities may also ensue. Depending upon the nature of the chemical agent, a spectrum of physiological and psychological symptoms may become prominent including skin lesions, respiratory distress, and psychophysiological signs. Concerns related to water and food contamination may add to fear reactions in the community.

Explosives attack: During the immediate impact period, injuries and deaths related to the blast wave, shrapnel and flying debris, and severe burns would challenge emergency response. Individuals may be trapped in collapsed structures and burning vehicles or buried in rubble. There may be secondary attacks to increase terror, timed to interfere with rescue efforts and harm responders. Fears of recurrence would lead to feelings of uncertainty, fear and anxiety. Survivors and first responders alike would be exposed to respiratory hazards from clouds of debris hovering over the impact zone and toxins that have been released into the atmosphere. The recovery, restoration and reconstruction period would be protracted and psychologically difficult.

The Oklahoma City bombing graphically portrays the indiscriminate killing of innocents and the vulnerability of children. Nineteen children were killed and 200 children lost one or both parents. Over 60 percent of school children surveyed in nearby schools reported that they heard or felt the explosion and more than one-third knew someone who was injured or killed (Pfefferbaum et al., 2002). Repeated television exposure to news reports of the bombing heightened the risk of posttraumatic stress symptoms (Pfefferbaum et al., 2001).

Source: FEMA Photo Library

Bioterrorism: Bioterrorism has been defined as "the premeditated unlawful use or threat of use of a biological organism" with the intent to terrorize or to kill the defined enemy (Culpepper, 2001). Depending on the infectious agent and its route of delivery on an unsuspecting community, varying devastating effects may occur from a biological attack (Shaw, 2003). If the infectious agent is transmissible person-to-person, some of the outcomes may be analogous to those discussed for pandemics.

The use of infectious agents as instruments of war was first noted historically at the time of the "Black Death", when a seaport town under siege attempted to repel the invaders by catapulting bodies infected with bubonic plague over the walls as "bubonic germ warfare missiles" (Cantor, 2001). The first bioterrorist attack against the United States occurred in 1984 when a religious cult in Oregon contaminated the salad bars of 10 local restaurants with Salmonella with the intention of incapacitating many residents so that they would not be able to vote on a referendum unfavorable to the cult (Siegrist & Graham, 2000). While biological agents may be used to kill or severely sicken a population, they may also be used as a threat to extort a population to carry out the will of the biological terrorists. The "Category A" agents of greatest concern as identified by the Centers for Disease Control and Prevention are Bacillus anthracis (anthrax), Yersinia pestis (plague), Francisella tularensis (tularemia), Clostridium botulinum (botulism) toxin, smallpox virus, and viral hemorrhagic fever viruses (such as Ebola and Marburg) (Moran, 2000a,b; Culpepper, 2001). Scientists estimate that over 60 pathogens are capable of being weaponized with varying degrees of lethality and capacity for contagion.

Four methods may be used to deploy biological weapons: 1) food contamination, 2) water contamination, 3) aerosol delivery, and 4) person-to-person spread. Food and water supplies may also be contaminated through the poisoning of livestock (Stern, 1999). While many assume that the technical expertise necessary to aerosolize microorganisms into dry powders or to create liquid slurries is beyond the capabilities of most terrorist groups, surface-modified anthrax spores were placed in envelopes and successfully mailed to United States media outlets and government officials in 2001, resulting in a total of five deaths among 23 persons who became infected. The Centers for Disease Control and Prevention placed more than 30,000 postal workers, government and media employees on a prophylactic regimen of antibiotics. All three branches of the Federal government were shut down for periods of time and millions of pieces of mail were embargoed and delayed in processing. Tens of thousands of excess Hazmat calls were generated throughout the United States as citizens became excessively worried about white powders and "puffy" envelopes. Large numbers of persons purchased and hoarded antibiotic medications. Public anxiety was widespread.

Pre-impact terrorism stressors. Acts of terrorism and bioterrorism occur sporadically and unpredictably, with very low prevalence in most areas. Terrorist acts are episodic, reflecting a manifestation of a political and ideological readiness to employ "asymmetrical" violence to achieve the group's goals. The predominant stressor for families and their children in the pre-impact phase is uncertainty coupled with anxiety. A study in Israel noted that the uncertainty of where a terrorist act will occur results in comparable risks for posttraumatic stress symptoms for persons living in areas where terrorist attacks have and have not previously occurred (Shalev et al., 2006).

Impact stressors: Terrorism is psychological by design (Shultz et al., 2007). "The goal of terrorism is to terrorize," (IOM, 2003). Each type of terrorist-perpetrated weapon of mass destruction is associated with a unique constellation of stressors. Understandably, survivors of terrorism experience extreme fear and distress compounded with intense feelings of helplessness, anger, and distrust. In the aftermath survivors struggle to find meaning in the experience. Stressors include exposure to brutal death on a mass scale (including deaths of children), personal harm, illness and physical debility. Acts of terrorism separate and displace loved ones and disrupt the routines of everyday life including school, home and work. Feelings of biological fragility and psychological vulnerability are common.

Children are often uniquely susceptible to human-generated acts of violence. Diminutive size and limited motor skills of young children hamper their ability to escape from harm's way during extreme events of all types. Children may not have the cognitive abilities to realistically evaluate risk; in fact, curiosity may actually attract them toward danger. Children's larger surface-to-mass ratio increases a variety of risks, such as hypothermia, dehydration, and exposure to hazardous materials.

Post-impact terrorism stressors. The degree of devastation resulting from terrorist attacks may vary from highly-focused damage from an improvised explosive device to the wholesale destruction of a community following a nuclear detonation, bioterrorist or chemical attack. Depending on the scope and extent of the devastation rendered by a terrorist act, the community will confront a fairly predictable cascade of secondary stressors (Shaw, 2003, 2004). Families and communities should not underestimate the cumulative effects of terror, fear and the uncertainty of future terrorist actions. Subsequent to a major terrorist attack are the issues related to evacuation, displacement, relocation, and rebuilding. Communities may experience loss of access to basic needs such as food and water and disruption of vital services such as electrical

power, transportation, and health care. Efforts to contend with these adversities may significantly deplete resiliency, coping and emotional resources. In the aftermath, many families may grapple with death, disabling illness or injury, or loss of home or valued possessions. Family functioning may change, as manifested by marital problems, domestic violence, substance abuse, financial hardship, and demoralization. Multiple, compounding losses are common following human-generated disasters, frequently leading to feelings of depression and vulnerability. Rates of substance abuse, delinquent acts, and interpersonal violence may rise.

In the aftermath of terrorism, the continuity of ecological and psychosocial disruption will continue unabated long after the impact phase. Terrorist actions may lead to severe economic downturns and unemployment that will produce long-term family hardships. Family support and social networks may disintegrate as people are displaced and relocated. Survivors may be relegated to living in public shelters with great uncertainty regarding their ability to return to home, school, or work. Life and family routines will be dismantled. Perceived personal and family security will be undermined.

Traumatic reminders. Individuals who have directly experienced terrorist attacks are vulnerable to sudden, unexpected exposure to traumatic reminders that resonate with the trauma event.

Source: FEMA Photo Library

Source: FEMA Photo Library

Complex Emergencies

War-related Trauma

War is one of the constants of human history, a product of the competitive struggle for territory, resources and power (Durant & Durant, 1968). At any time in history, war is an ongoing reality for some populations but a seemingly remote possibility for others. Yet war may come suddenly and unexpectedly to unsuspecting populations not previously engaged in conflict. War invariably destroys the socioeconomic fabric of the community, disrupting moral codes, embedded patterns of relationships and shared values (de Jong, 2002). The impact of war cuts across all levels of society. Individuals exposed to war-related traumas experience the same range of psychological responses as those exposed to other forms of trauma.

As civil strife proliferates, and civilians become its main causalities, millions of children are growing up in families and communities torn apart by armed conflict. Since 1990, conflicts have directly killed 3.6 million people and 45 per cent of these have been children. Hundreds of thousands of children are caught up in armed conflict. Some children are conscripted to serve as soldiers. Others are displaced by war, becoming refugees or internally displaced persons. Children in war-torn countries suffer sexual violence, abuse and exploitation. Children may be maimed or killed by the explosive remnants of war. UNICEF estimates that 90 per cent of global conflict-related deaths since 1990 have been non-combatant civilian deaths. Women and children comprise 80 percent of civilian war-related deaths (UNICEF, 2005). It has been reported that two million children have been killed in wars, 5 million have been disabled and 12 million have been left homeless (UNICEF, 1997).

War-related traumas are diverse, accumulate over time, and have an immediate and enduring psychological effect on children. The most powerful predictors of adverse psychological effects of war are the intensity and the duration of exposure to war-related traumatic events (Hadi & Llabre, 1998; Thabet & Vostanis, 1999; Vizek-Vidovi et al., 2000; Yule, 2000; Smith et al., 2001). It is generally estimated that among children exposed to war-related stressors, the prevalence of posttraumatic stress

symptomatology varies from 10-90 percent, subsuming anxiety disorders such as PTSD, depression, disruptive behaviors and somatic symptoms (Goldstein et al., 1997; Hadi & Liabre, 1998; de Jong, 2002). In war, more children die from starvation, sickness, and the stress of flight than from physical injury and violence.

Stressors Faced by Children in Wartime

- Lack of adequate food, shelter and medical care
- Separation from caregivers
- Injury to self
- Injury or death of a family member
- Persecution and exposure to violence
- Forced displacement from home
- Separation from friends and community
- Inadequate substitute care-giving following parental loss
- Lack of economic security
- Denial of educational opportunities
- Exploitation
- Physical or sexual abuse

Source: Duncan and Arntson, 2004

Refugees and Internally Displaced Populations:

Approximately 80-90 percent of all victims of warfare today are women and children (Lustig et al., 2002). Many seek safety and shelter as an escape from war, destruction of home, hunger, disease and persecution.

There are 22 million **refugees** throughout the world, half of whom are children. Civilians are defined as refugees when they cross an international frontier to seek sanctuary in another country. Refugees in flight are frequently exposed to brutal death, the traumatic effects of perilous escape, violence and hardship including physical injury, mutilation, rape, and malnutrition. Newly-arrived refugees normally receive food, shelter and a place of safety from the host country. Many refugees are temporarily settled in camp environments where crowding, poor nutrition, poverty, enforced passivity, unemployment, boredom, discrimination and continuous exposure to violence and

Table 2.2 Top 10 Countries with Refugees 2006 (UNHCR)	
Pakistan	1,044,462
Iran	968,370
United States	843,498
Syria	702,209
Germany	605,406
Jordan	500,229
Tanzania	485,295
United Kingdom	301,556
China	301,027
Chad	286,743

Source: UNHCR, 2006

There are millions of other civilians who are classified as **internally displaced persons (IDPs).** These persons take flight from home and seek shelter and safety within the boundaries of their own country. Currently, there is an estimated total of 23.7 million IDPs, living amidst war and persecution in more than 50 countries (de Jong, 2002). IDPs have minimal legal or physical protection and a very uncertain future, existing as outcasts in their own countries. IDPs face a difficult and uncertain future, trapped in an ongoing internal conflict. The domestic government, which may view the uprooted people as 'enemies of the state,' retains ultimate control of their fate. There are no specific international legal instruments covering human rights for IDPs and general agreements such as the Geneva Conventions are often difficult to apply. Humanitarian agencies may be barred from providing support and philanthropic donors may be reluctant to intervene in internal conflicts or offer sustained assistance.

death are parts of the daily landscape. The United Nations and other humanitarian organizations work within this legal framework to help refugees restart their lives in a new state or eventually return home. Studies of war refugee children and their families have revealed a range of psychiatric disorders including posttraumatic stress disorders, mood disorders, anxiety reactions, disruptive behaviors and somatoform disorders (Weine et al., 1995; Goldin et al., 2001).

For example, 75,000 Bosnian refugees (one-third were children) sought asylum in Sweden (Goldin et al., 2001). The exile experience for these refugees included living in temporary sorting camps followed by transfer to crowded military barracks. In addition to culture shock, refugee status in a new country is associated with separation from loved ones, loss of native language and customs, xenophobia, poverty, and a downward spiral of social and professional mobility.

Table 2.3 Top 12 Internally Displaced Populations of Concern to UNHCR, 2005	
Colombia	2,000,000
Iraq	1,200,000
Sudan	841,900
Azerbaijan	578,500
Somalia	400,000
Sri Lanka	324,700
Serbia & Montenegro	246,400
Liberia	237,800
Georgia	234,200
Bosnia & Herzegovina	182,700
Russian Fed.	170,500
Afghanistan	142,500

Source: UNHCR, 2006

Trauma Risks for Refugee and IDP Children

Risks for refugee or IDP children:
- Risk of malnutrition
- Increased risk of disease and physical injury
- Lack of protection and increased risk of physical or sexual violence
- Discrimination
- Lack of educational opportunities
- Emotional risks due to exposure to death, injury, multiple losses, bereavement, loss of community and/or country affiliation

Special situations with higher risks for refugee and IDP children:
- Coercion to become a child soldier
- Child labor (hard physical labor, duties involving high danger, begging, prostitution)
- Slavery following sale by child traffickers

Source: UNICEF , 2007

Child Soldiers:

Of particular interest to mental health professions who work with child survivors of trauma are those children who become child soldiers. Child soldiers are both the victims of war and the perpetuators of violence. There are over 300,000 child soldiers less than 18 years of age engaged in various conflicts in over 50 countries. It is estimated that there are a 100,000 child soldiers in Africa alone who have participated in warring conflicts in Sierra Leone, Liberia, Mozambique, Somalia, Congo and Uganda. The military use of children dates back to ancient history. Well-known historic examples include David's service to King Saul, French drummer boys in Napoleon's army, young boys who served as "powder monkeys" on the ships of the Royal Navy, and the Hitler Youth (Hitlerjugend) in Nazi Germany who were formed into combat units for the defense of Berlin.

Children are especially vulnerable to recruitment because of their emotional and physical immaturity. Many are refugees, displaced from home, separated from families,

Congo Brazzaville : civil war 2004 © EC/ECHO/François Goemans

orphaned, or otherwise have little means of support or access to education or employment. Children may be abducted or seized from the streets, villages, schools and orphanages. The child militias become a source of security; a surrogate family; and a guarantor of meals, clothing and shelter. Once recruited, children often serve as porters, cooks, couriers, spotters, and spies, human shields and recently, suicide bombers. Technological advances in weaponry have led to the development of lightweight automatic weapons which are simple to operate and can be easily used by children. In battle, child soldiers are often pushed forward as cannon fodder and suffer high casualty rates from enemy fire and land mines.

Many of these children have been forced to commit acts of violence to prove their fidelity to the group. Exposure to brutal aggressive violence against others at such an early age may leave children damaged in terms of their moral sense regarding violence (Shaw, 1994; de Silva, 2001). The child warriors are often the most feared of all the soldiers as they have been acculturated to violence and have few scruples about killing (Shaw & Harris, 2003). The derivative effects of exposure to war-related stressors on the developing child are far-ranging and may effect the elaboration and consolidation of personality traits, identity formation, adaptive and coping mechanisms, internalized standards of right and wrong, intrinsic mechanisms for modulating aggressive impulses, and the child's habitual mode of relating to others, as well as having enduring neurobiological consequences.

Bayer et al. (2007) studied 169 former child soldiers. The average child soldier had been violently abducted into the Lord's Resistance Army at 12 years of age and had served, on average, for three years. Three-fourths of these children reported one or more of these experiences: threats of being killed, serious injury, or witnessing a friend or family member being killed. Over half had killed others. The authors noted that child soldiers with the most posttraumatic stress symptoms were less likely to be open to "reconciliation" with the enemy and harbored more aggressive vengeful fantasies. The authors conclude, "posttraumatic stress might hinder the children's ability to deal with and overcome emotions of hate and revenge" and thus lessen the opportunity to seek peaceful ways to resolve conflict.

While there is a need to support the continuing effort of human rights groups and governments to support the Rome Statute of the International Criminal Court (1998) making it a war crime to conscript or enlist children less than 15 years of age for armed conflict, the adoption of international legislation banning the recruitment of child soldiers will not ensure an end to recruitment. Campaigning against the exploitation of children as combatants on the global stage must be supported by the sensitive reintegration into civil society of children who have participated in armed conflicts. Former child combatants have often been denied critical developmental and educational experiences facilitative to a successful reintegration to community life. It is essential that government and international resources focus on developing programs to ensure psychosocial and medical care, educational opportunities, literacy, and occupational skills training for former child soldiers. Yet these reintegration components have received less financial support than disarmament and demobilization efforts, an imbalance that can lead to frustration and further violence (UNICEF, 2005).

DRC: Bunia riots
2003 © EC/ECHO/François Goemans

Summary

Disaster is defined as a severe ecological and psychosocial disruption which greatly exceeds the coping capacity of the altered community. The universe of disasters is generally divided into two broad categories, natural disasters and human-generated disasters and in this discussion, expanded to include "complex emergencies." Disasters occur across a time-line with specific phases. The pre-impact phase is associated with planning and preparedness as well as providing warnings when a disaster is imminent. The impact phase is characterized by the encounter with the disaster's "forces of harm", creating the peak threat of bodily injury, death, property damage and community disruption. The post-impact phase brings a cascade of secondary stressors associated with multiple losses and ongoing adversities. The psychological outcomes for children and adults are shaped by the distinguishing features of each type of disaster, as well as the unique characteristics of the specific disaster event. Traumatic reminders are often triggered by the specific nuances associated with the disaster.

Chapter 3

The Context of Trauma

On successful completion of this chapter you should be able to:

1) Recognize that psychological effects of trauma are mediated through a myriad of contextual factors
2) Describe the three components of the Disaster Ecology Model
3) Provide examples of risk and protective factors operating at individual, family, community, and societal levels
4) Recognize the relationship between degree of exposure to disaster and severity of psychological consequences

Key Concepts

- The child's psychological response to a potentially injurious or life-threatening disaster is influenced by contextual factors at the individual, family, community, and societal levels.
- Within each level, risk factors exacerbate psychological responses while protective factors mitigate the impact of disaster.
- The Disaster Ecology Model portrays the encounter between forces of harm and children and families in harm's way in relation to the ecological context.
- The Population Exposure Model portrays the relationship between degree of exposure and extent of psychological consequences.
- Any disaster affecting the family has reverberating effects on the child.
- Poverty and race/ethnic minority status elevate disaster risks at every stage.

Colombia: Narino (Tumako) - settlement of internally displaced people 2005 © EC/ECHO/Karin Michotte

Children: Stress, Trauma and Disasters

Introduction

The child's psychological response to a potentially injurious or life-threatening disaster is influenced by the complex array of contextual factors operating at individual, family, community and societal levels. Within each level, risk factors exacerbate psychological responses while protective factors mitigate the impact of disaster.

For children, individual factors include age, gender, race, educational level, medical and psychiatric history, previous history of trauma, and level of functioning before and during the disaster. The child filters the disaster experience differently depending upon the current stage of cognitive development and level of understanding of disaster causation. Family factors are particularly relevant determinants of the child's response to trauma and disaster. Included here are family structure and family cohesiveness, communication patterns, parental response to disaster impact and post-disaster family functioning. Community and societal factors include culture, ethnicity, socioeconomic status, political structure and governance, social support networks, and post-disaster community functioning.

The Disaster Ecology Model

Disaster ecology incorporates the principles of social ecology and examines the interrelationships and interdependence of the social, psychological, anthropological, cultural, geographic, economic, and human context surrounding disasters and extreme public health events (Shultz, et al., 2007).

Many aspects of the environment influence the child's life and behavior. Children exist within a family unit that connects to other systems: extended family, friends and peers, local neighborhoods, schools and larger surrounding communities. All of these systems exert influences on the child although the greatest influences tend to come from those life systems that are closest to the child. For example, for many children, the family unit is the most central and influential, followed by the network of friends and peers,

followed by the school and local neighborhood. The social ecological perspective supports the contention that the child's psychological and social response to disaster and trauma is determined by influences that operate and interconnect at many levels including individual, family, community and societal.

The Disaster Ecology Model (Shultz, et al., 2007) was developed to explicitly examine how disasters simultaneously produce an array of physical, medical, psychological, and behavioral effects. The three components of the Model are 1) the forces of harm, 2) the affected population in harm's way, and 3) the ecological context. The Model provides a framework for simultaneously considering the interrelationships among these three components:

Components of the Disaster Ecology Model	
Forces of Harm	Disaster hazards
Children and families in harm's way	Children directly threatened or impacted by the forces of harm, or indirectly sustaining loss and change associated with the disaster event
Ecological Context	Risk and resiliency factors, operating at many levels, that influence the degree of physical and psychological harm sustained during a disaster or extreme event

The remainder of this chapter discusses the elements that comprise the Disaster Ecology Model, focusing on the exposure and context factors that shape the psychosocial responses to disasters (Table 3.1).

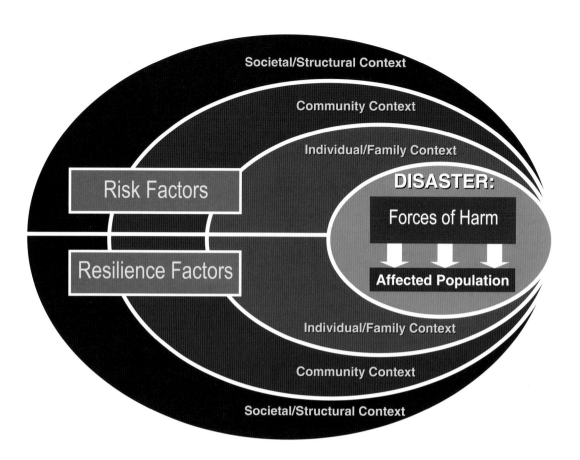

Table 3.1 Factors that Shape Psychosocial Responses to Disasters			
Exposure Factors	**Individual Factors**	**Family Factors**	**Community/Societal Factors**
• Intensity and duration of exposure • Direct involvement in the disaster • Separation from loved ones and caretakers • Witnessing the event • Knowing someone who was injured or killed • Personal injury • Exposure to brutal death and gruesome scenes • Degree of life threat • Child's subjective experience at the time of exposure • Exposure through the media	• Age • Gender • Cognitive and maturational development • Pre-disaster presence of psychopathology • History of exposure to traumatic events • Subjective appraisal of the stressor • Social support • Effectiveness of adaptive and coping styles	• Parental response • Parent symptom choice • Family atmosphere • Parental over-protectiveness • Separation from parents and siblings • Prohibitive response to regression • Reversal of the dependency role	• School community • Social support networks • Community socio-economic status • Political structure and governance • Culture/ ethnicity

1. Exposure Factors

The most powerful predictor of psychological morbidity in children is the intensity and duration of traumatic exposure. Magnitude of exposure relates to such factors as proximity to the zone of impact, personal injury, death or injury to family members or loved ones, separation from caretakers, degree of perceived life threat, and the psychological responses of parents or family members (the "contagion" effect).

The survivor's subjective appraisal of the disaster or trauma experience also relates to the occurrence of adverse psychological effects. How the individual defines the traumatic situation, and the meaning he or she imposes on the event, are strong predictors of outcome. Feelings of helplessness, hopelessness and panic, and the conviction that one is going to die, increase the risk of psychological morbidly in the aftermath of disaster (Pfefferbaum et al., 2002; Yule & Udwin, 1991; Watson & Shalev, 2005).

Table 3.2 Exposure Risk Factors

- Intensity and duration of exposure
- Direct involvement in the event
- Separation from loved ones and caretakers
- Witnessing the event
- Knowing someone who was injured or killed
- Personal injury
- Exposure to brutal death and gruesome scenes
- Degree of life threat
- Child's subjective experience at the time of exposure
- Exposure through the media

In the Population Exposure Model, the degree of exposure is portrayed using a color gradient, with inner rings of extreme exposure presented in shades of red and progressively larger rings "cooling" toward the greens and blues. The model visually reflects research findings that "the individuals who are most personally, physically,

and psychologically exposed to trauma and the disaster scene are likely to be affected the most," (DHHS, 2002, 2004). Exposure to a traumatic stressor may be the result of on-scene physical impact, witnessing the event directly, media exposure or interpersonal connectedness to the disaster victims (Pine & Cohen, 2002). Exposure and psychological distress extend far beyond the impact zone to include persons distant from the scene and remotely connected to the event.

The Population Exposure Model

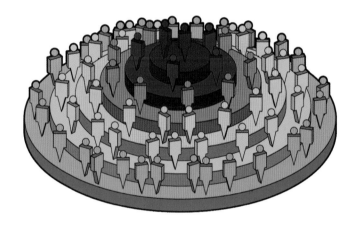

Sources: DHHS, 2004, 2005

▶ Community victims killed and seriously injured. Bereaved family members, loved ones, close friends.
▶ Community victims exposed to the incident and disaster scene, but not injured.
▶ Bereaved extended family members and friends. Residents in disaster zone whose homes were destroyed. Rescue and recovery workers. Medical examiner's office staff. Service providers immediately involved with bereaved families or obtaining information for body identification and death notification.
▶ Mental health providers. Clergy. Chaplains. Emergency health care providers. Government officials. Members of the media.
▶ Groups that identify with the target-victim group. Businesses.
▶ Community at large.

Direct impact survivors: Aligned with Population Exposure Model, for children, severity of posttraumatic stress symptoms has been found to be directly related to their proximity to the zone of impact. As examples, the highest rates of posttraumatic stress symptoms were found for:

• Children inside a movie theatre that was hit by a tornado (Bloch et al, 1956)
• Children who were closest to a jungle gym on the playground where a child was killed during a school shooting (Pynoos et al., 1987)
• Children in the immediate path of raging Australian bush fires (McFarlane, 1987)
• Children exposed to the peak winds in the "eyewall" of Hurricane Andrew (Shaw, 1995, 1996)
• Children who were trapped in attics and stranded in flood zones during Hurricane Katrina, including those who believed they were going to die, those who were physically injured, those who lost their homes and were displaced, those who lost a parent or family member to death from Katrina and those who were separated from parents and caregivers during and after the storm.

Direct witnesses: These individuals are visual witnesses but not directly harmed in terms of injury, property loss or loss of a family member. Adults and children who directly observed the collapse of the World Trade Center towers on September 11, 2001 or observed persons jumping from the upper floors of the towers were direct witnesses.

Indirectly exposed: Children who are physically distant from the site of disaster but have familial or friendship bonds with an individual who is injured or killed are at risk for psychological trauma.

Disaster responders: This includes the first-line responders, rescue and recovery workers, emergency health care services providers, government officials, members of the media, and mental health professionals. The Population Exposure Model makes salient the fact that disaster survivors and disaster responders alike are affected psychologically during extreme events. First line responders are unusually vulnerable to psychological impact as they quickly respond to cries for help; are exposed to the powerful images, sounds, and smells of the disaster scene; and provide assistance during a mass causality event. This is relevant for children because first-line responders are also parents. Moreover, children may witness, directly or through media viewing, the powerful reactions experienced by responders.

The community at large: Posttraumatic symptom expression extended beyond persons who were directly exposed to the September 11, 2001 attacks to also include hundreds of thousands of residents of the New York City boroughs who were distant from the scene and only indirectly exposed (Galea and Resnick, 2005). A nationwide survey of children throughout the United States, ages 5 to 18, conducted three to five days after the September 11, 2001 attack, found that 35 percent reported at least one symptom of posttraumatic stress such as irritability, nightmares, avoiding hearing or talking about what happened, sleep problems or trouble concentrating (Schuster et al., 2001). A larger survey of 8,266 children in grades 4 through 12, conducted by the New York City Department of Health and Mental Hygiene, indicated that PTSD increased from a baseline of 2 percent to 10.5 percent, separation anxiety disorder doubled, and agoraphobia tripled following the attacks (Fremont, 2004).

Not only does direct, on-scene exposure produce psychological consequences but indirect exposure via television and media coverage or close interpersonal ties to a disaster victim may also produce distress and impairment. Television viewing is a very powerful indirect source of exposure (Pfefferbaum et al., 2001; Schuster et al., 2001). Routine television viewing of traumatic situations can generate fear reactions and sleep disturbances among preschoolers and elementary school-age children. Television viewing of the Challenger space shuttle explosion (Terr et al., 1999), the Oklahoma City Bombing (Pfefferbaum et al., 2001) and the terrorist attack on the World Trade Center was associated with emotional, behavioral and stress-related symptoms.

2. Individual Factors

At the individual level, the effects of trauma on children and adolescents relate to the nature of the exposure, mediated by an array of child-specific factors including the child's gender, cognitive and maturational development, pre-disaster coping skills, subjective appraisal of the stressor, history of psychiatric disorders, prior exposure to traumatic events, ability to elicit and use caretaker support, and the effectiveness of current adaptive and coping styles (Pine & Cohen, 2002).

Table 3.3 Individual Risk Factors

- Female gender
- History of separation or separation anxiety
- Limited cognitive and maturational development
- Limited pre-disaster coping skills
- Negative subjective appraisal of the stressor
- History of psychiatric disorders
- Prior exposure to traumatic events
- Limited ability to elicit and use caretaker support
- Limited effectiveness of current adaptive and coping skills

Gender effects: Boys are more likely to be exposed to traumatic events. Upon exposure, girls are more inclined to manifest higher rates of anxiety and mood symptoms and to meet diagnostic criteria for PTSD (Green et al., 1991; Shaw et al., 1995, 1996; Pine & Cohen, 2002). Shaw et al. (1996) found some evidence that while boys recovered more quickly from PTSD after Hurricane Andrew, boys manifested more disruptive behaviors than girls. Gender differences were also found in children's response to war-related trauma: girls exposed to the war in Croatia showed more symptoms of anxiety and depression while the boys manifested a lower level of psychosocial adaptation (Vizek-Vidovic et al., 2000).

Pre-existing psychopathology: Children with a history of emotional and behavioral problems (particularly anxiety disorders), cognitive impairment, learning disorders, separation anxiety, or depression are at higher risk for psychological consequences following disasters.

Prior trauma exposure: In contrast to Nietzsche's aphorism, "that which does not kill you makes you stronger", the reality is that trauma exposure usually does not have an inoculation effect. In fact, repeated trauma exposure tends to produce a cumulative detrimental effect with loss of resilience and increased vulnerability to future trauma exposure.

Subjective appraisal: The child's subjective experience at the time of exposure to the traumatic situation is a predictor of psychological response. For adolescents onboard the sinking ship, *Jupiter*, the predictors of adverse psychological reactions were thinking that they would not escape, panic feelings and fear of dying (Udwin et al., 2000). The most prevalent and distressing subjective appraisals reported by middle-school children following the Oklahoma City Bombing were fear that someone in the family would be hurt, fear that a friend would be hurt, and feeling nervous and afraid (Pfefferbaum et al., 2002). These "peri-traumatic" responses were stronger predictors of adverse psychological outcomes than immediate physical exposure, relationship to a victim, and television viewing of the bombing.

Protective factors: Despite trauma exposure many children are able to adapt and regain full function with only minimal symptoms. Protective factors include the child's capacity to recognize and avoid dangers; personal resiliency (the capability to restore pre-trauma psychological equilibrium); capacity to manage anxiety; ability to use adults for caretaking activities; degree of social, community and family cohesiveness; and shared values and beliefs with those around them.

3. Family Factors

Since children are so dependent on parents and the family system, any disaster affecting the family has reverberating effects on the child (McFarlane, 1987; Green et al., 1991; Shaw 2000, 2003). The family's caretaker role is substantially compromised when the family is impacted by death, parental illness, or separation from loved ones, and when parents are emotionally distressed.

Children often mirror the anxiety and symptom choices of their parents. A number of parental behaviors and symptoms have been associated with increased risk of psychological distress among children, such as parental psychopathology, family emotional atmosphere, parental over-protectiveness, reversal of the dependency role and excessive prohibition of regressive behaviors (Shaw, 2000). McFarlane (1987) found that the mother's psychological response to an Australian bushfire disaster was a better predictor of the child's psychological response than the child's direct exposure. It is generally agreed that the presence of parental psychopathology and family dysfunction predicts higher levels of psychological morbidity in children. The psychological response of Lebanese children (5-7 years of age) exposed to war-related trauma was best predicted by the level of depressive symptoms in their mothers (Bryce et al., 1989). Conversely, the existence of parental and family support mitigates the risk for posttraumatic stress symptoms. Other family features that effect psychological outcomes for children are marital conflict and instability, low socio-economic status, family history of neuroticism, and single parent home.

The reactions of children exposed to war-related trauma provide insights into children's reactions to disaster. War, which undermines the child's sense of security, has a devastating and enduring effect on the family and the social fabric of a community. In situations of war, family factors, mediated by social contexts such as displacement, play a crucial role in shaping the child's psychological response. Indeed, contextual factors interact with war-related traumas as a mediator of children's psychological response. Almqvist and Broberg (1999) found that the degree of family support predicts children's long-term emotional response to being a refugee. Higher rates of psychological morbidity were found among displaced Israeli families compared with non-displaced families with comparable levels of exposure to the Scud missile attacks during the 1991 Gulf War (Loar, Womer & Cohen, 2001).

Table 3.4 Family Factors

Pre-event	Post-event
• Family atmosphere • Parental psychopathology • Over-protectiveness • Dysfunctional parents • Marital instability • Single parent household • Low socioeconomic status • Family history of neuroticism (proneness to experience irritability, depression, and anxiety)	• Parent symptom choice • Separation from parents, caretakers or siblings • Prohibitive response to regression • Reversal of the dependency role • Multiple stressors (loss of home, property and financial loss) • Prolonged displacement • Continued separation and estrangement from family and friends • Resource deterioration • Marital distress • Decline in perceived social support • Financial distress (unemployment)

4. Community/Societal Factors

Community refers to a social context with its network of relationships but more importantly, it refers to shared values, understandings and a common outlook as to what is important in life. A number of authors have observed the devastating psychological effects of disaster on a community and the ever-widening circles of involvement as one moves from directly-exposed individuals to family members, friends, neighbors, first-line responders, and the surrounding community of individuals who are distressed and suffer vicariously (Erikson, 1976; Taylor & Fraser 1981; Wright et al., 1990). The child's psychological vulnerability mirrors that of the community at large. Community disruption creates a broad composite of secondary stressors (Table 3.5). The loss of the school community through school closures, disrupted school activities, and emotionally distressed teachers and staff, represents a significant adversity for children (Pynoos et al., 1998).

The impact ratio in a disaster is the number of disaster victims as a proportion of all citizens in the disaster-affected community. The impact ratio serves as a predictor of adverse psychosocial outcomes for survivors at the level of the total community. In a study of ten eastern Kentucky counties affected by a widespread flood, the impact ratio consistently predicted rates of depression, anxiety, and somatic symptoms after controlling for the effects of personal loss. Survivors who fared most poorly were those who experienced high levels of personal loss in combination with high levels of community destruction. The capacity of survivors to cope and recover resonates with a number of factors associated with the community's "social surround," the combination of social support, socioeconomic status, political structure, governance, and culture/ethnicity (Somasundaram et al., 2003).

It is generally estimated that about 25-75 percent of individuals in a disaster impact zone will have a significant "stress response" that will temporarily compromise functioning during the impact phase and in the immediate aftermath. As many as 30-40 percent will continue to have significant psychological morbidity in the year following disaster (World Health Organization, 1992).

Alexander (2004) has suggested that in some instances, the effects of the disaster are so far-reaching, that the catastrophic impact becomes transformational. Powerful historical examples include Hiroshima, the Holocaust, September 11, 2001, the Indian Ocean tsunami, and Hurricane Katrina. Alexander states, "cultural trauma occurs when members of a collectivity feel they have been subjected to a horrendous event that leaves indelible marks upon their group consciousness, marking their memories forever and changing their future identity in fundamental and irrevocable ways."

Social and community support: Each child, and the family unit as a whole, is affected by the quality of social supports and social infrastructure. Disasters may produce devastating effects on available social supports through breakdown of communication channels, displacement of populations, separation of loved ones, death and debilitating injury. The child may be impacted by the closure of schools and community programs where children congregate. Somasundaram et al. (2003) have observed that "disaster victims often find it difficult to maintain supportive relationships just when they need them the most". In the aftermath of Hurricane Andrew, rates of divorce and family violence increased. Within a community, disaster recovery is more challenging for families of minority status, single-parent families, families with persons with special needs, and displaced or refugee families.

Socio-economic status and poverty: The unfavorable association between poverty and mental health has been described worldwide throughout history (Costello et al., 2003). Socioeconomic disadvantage negatively affects children's mental health and is associated with decreased intelligence, academic achievement, and social and emotional functioning (Gilliam et al., 2007). Family and neighborhood poverty is associated with a poor physical home environment and insufficient parental warmth, thus adversely affecting children's mental health. Behavior problems such as disobedience, interpersonal conflict, and rules violations are more prevalent for children in households with low socioeconomic status (Achenbach et al., 1987). The negative influences of socioeconomic disadvantage on child behavior are mediated by chronic exposure to stress and uncertainty and by dysfunctional

Buffalo Creek Disaster: Loss of Community

Kai Erikson (1976) described the after-effects of the Buffalo Creek, West Virginia flood, which occurred on February 26, 1972. Following torrential rains, a slag dam ruptured, sending millions of gallons of water cascading down a narrow mountain hollow. Without warning, flood waters destroyed a series of villages downstream from the dam. Survivors described the experience of losing their homes and simultaneously losing their sense of community.

"We was like one big family. Like when somebody was hurt, everybody was hurt. You know I guess it was because it was the same people all the time. I don't know how to explain it. It's a good feeling. It's more than friends. If someone was hurt, everybody was concerned, everybody. If somebody lost a member of their family, they were always there. Everybody was around bringing you something to eat, to help. It's a deeper feeling".

"We did lose a community, and I mean it was a good community. Everybody was close, everybody knowed everybody. But now everybody is alone. They act like they're lost. They lost their homes and their way of life...the people are all scattered. You can't go next door and talk...there is no next door. You can't laugh with friends. You can't do that no more, because there's no friends around to laugh with."

"Well, I have lost all my friends. The people I was raised up and lived with, they're scattered. I don't know where they're at. I've got to make new friends, and that is a hard thing to do. You don't make new friends and feel towards them like you did with the people you lived with...but down here, there ain't but a few people I know, and you don't feel secure around people you don't know"

The town destroyed in the flood's aftermath was described as a "ghost town, a dreary hollow, a graveyard...it changed from a community of paradise to Death Valley".

Erikson (1976) noted that the "disaster syndrome", with its prominent features of numbness, apathy, and depression, is a reaction to the knowledge that one's community has been destroyed. To the individual survivor it is as if one's whole world has been destroyed. The visible community is in ruins.

parenting practices that are harsh, punitive, inconsistent and unsupportive (Boyle & Lipman, 2002).

In addition, empirical data suggests that children from low-income families are more likely to suffer from chronic illnesses, mental health problems and disabilities than their affluent counterparts (Brooks-Gunn & Duncan, 1997; Duncan, Brooks-Gunn & Klebanov, 1994) and are less likely to have a regular source of medical care and preventive health care services (Oberg, Bryant & Bach, 1995). An inverse relationship exists between household income and emotional and behavioral problems in childhood (Gilliam et al., 2007). In general, poor children are more likely to exhibit anxiety, social withdrawal, depression and disruptive behaviors than more affluent children (Duncan et

al., 1994). Persistent poverty is more harmful to children's mental health than transient poverty because of greater economic deprivation (Brooks-Gunn & Duncan, 1997; McLeod & Shanahan, 1996).

Disasters directly impact the socioeconomic infrastructure of a community. Workplaces are destroyed, transportation and communication systems are damaged, unemployment increases and financial resources are diminished. Socioeconomic status is a significant predictor of both physical and the psychological impact of disaster (Fothergill & Peek, 2004). Low-income households and communities, often located in hazardous locales with minimal protection and few resources, are vulnerable to natural disasters. Once disaster has occurred, the low-income family is more vulnerable to its consequences than its more well-to-do counterpart.

A recent review of studies on the relationship between poverty and disasters in the United States revealed that socio-economic status is a significant predictor of the physical and psychological impacts of disaster. Poor families were more likely than others to have family mental health risk factors. In disaster, they were more likely to experience psychiatric and psychological symptoms, physical injury, death and extensive damage to dwellings, as well as to encounter more obstacles during disaster response, recovery and reconstruction (Fothergill and Peek, 2004).

At the time when Hurricane Katrina struck New Orleans, 38 percent of children under the age of 18 years were below the poverty level, including 17,000 children below the age of six (Golden, 2006). Many children (40 percent) were separated from family members and 13 percent did not know where their families were located. Among these children, those living in poverty were disproportionately represented.

Table 3.5 Community/Societal Stressors

Pre-event	Post-event
• Family atmosphere • Level of preparedness • Lack of emergency management system resources • Poverty • Lack of civil government leadership • Ethnic and racial disparities	• Loss of community infrastructure • Resource deterioration • Loss of health care services • Social support deterioration • Media attention • Closure of schools • Perceived or actual failure of government response

Source: FEMA Photo Library

Geography: Patterns of human settlement and housing construction play a role in determining vulnerability to disasters. For Hurricane Katrina, areas within New Orleans could be identified geographically as high-stress environments for families and youth based on limited employment opportunities, low educational attainment, high crime rates and poor health indicators (Curtis et al., 2007). These areas, definable before Katrina's impact, were precisely the areas that sustained the greatest disaster-related physical destruction, loss of life, injury, population displacement, interpersonal violence and looting. Much of this area has not been repopulated. The former residents have been broadly dispersed and the communities have ceased to exist in some cases. In fact, the "convergence" of multiple ecological, social, political and economic risk factors, all overlapping within a definable geographic area, led to high rates of mortality, physical illness and injury, and psychological impairment for residents of those areas (Walker & Warren, 2007).

Political Structure and Governance: Response and intervention following disaster exposure are greatly influenced by political structure and governance. A tension always exists between the responsibilities and resources of the national government and the disaster-affected local municipalities. Local governments often want the national resources but resent intrusion and regulatory guidelines.

Much of the impact of Hurricane Katrina on children reflected shortcomings in the planning and governance process (Dolan & Krug, 2006). Failures of planning included the inability of government to support children's healthcare services. Absence of viable evacuation strategies left many children unnecessarily in harm's way during the storm. The evacuation process that was improvised in the aftermath frequently separated children from parents and caregivers. No effective strategies were in place for reuniting children who were separated from their parents; a situation that was most egregious for separated infants and preverbal toddlers whose identities could not be readily confirmed to assure proper placement. Completely lacking were mental health interventions for children affected by Katrina, resources for non-English-speaking children, and customized care for children with special medical needs, leading to increased rates of death and morbidity (Dolan & Krug, 2006).

Culture/Ethnicity: Culture is defined as "the unique behavior patterns and lifestyle shared by a group of people, which distinguish it from others," while ethnicity refers to "social groups that distinguish themselves from other groups by a common historical path, behavior norms, and their own group identities," (Wseng, 2003). Culture "refers to manifest characteristic behavior patterns and value systems, whereas ethnicity refers to a group of people that share a common feature or root culture" (Wseng, 2003).

Approximately 70 percent of the United States population is composed of white, non-Hispanic citizens while the remaining 30 percent includes persons of African-American, Asian-American, Hispanic/Latino, and American Indian/Alaskan Native/Hawaiian Native ancestry.

Disaster is a social experience. Cultural groups, particularly those representing minorities or recent immigrants, experience the full range of disaster stressors and more. Added to challenges shared with members of the mainstream culture are additional stressors: language difficulties, lack of insurance, limited financial resources, discrimination from members of other cultural groups, unfamiliarity with community support systems, difficulty accessing disaster services, and immigration status issues. Recent immigrants may lack understanding of the systems of help that are available in their adopted culture. Members of some cultural groups are both marginalized and impoverished, increasing their vulnerability to the destructive forces of disaster. In disasters, ethnic minorities may experience more adverse psychological consequences than members of the majority culture (Norris & Alegria, 2005). Disadvantaged and minority populations have a higher rate and degree of exposure to pre-disaster trauma and are more vulnerable to subsequent trauma when disaster strikes (Breslau et al., 1998). In fact, ethnic communities face increased vulnerability to disaster hazards across all disaster phases (risk perception, preparedness, warning, physical impact, psychological impact, rescue, recovery, and reconstruction) (Fothergill et al., 1999). These findings prompted Cuttler (2005) to assert, "Disasters are income neutral and color-blind. Their impacts, however, are not."

Among children, ethnicity has been found to shape psychological outcomes following disasters. In an exhaustive review of the disaster literature, Norris et al. (2002) found four studies in which minority youth fared worse than majority youth (Garrison et al., 1995; La Greca, Silverman & Wasserstein, 1998; March et al.,1997; Shannon et al.,1994) and two studies in which the minority youth fared better (Garrison et al.,1993; Jones et al., 2001). Lengua et al. (2005) studied the psychological response of children following September 11, 2001, and noted that African-American children reported more avoidant posttraumatic stress symptoms and feelings of upset than Caucasian children.

Source: FEMA Photo Library

Chapter 3

Table 3.6 Risk Disparities for Ethnic Minorities by Disaster Stage

Disaster Stage	Impact on Ethnic Minorities
Preparedness behavior	**Preparedness** is the stage of the disaster life cycle encompassing all pre-event preparation activities and mitigation efforts in advance of a specific warning. **For ethnic minorities, preparedness risks may include:** • Lack of information in native language • Lack of financial resources to obtain preparedness materials • Living in areas more vulnerable to damage from disaster hazards
Warning communication and response	**The warning communication and response** stage entails receiving warnings or other risk communications regarding an immediate danger and taking some type of action in response to this warning, such as evacuation. **For ethnic minorities, warning communication and response risks may include:** • Lack of information in native language • Lack of transportation • Evacuation difficulties
Physical impacts	The **physical impact** stage is concerned with the actual and immediate effects of the disaster striking a community. Physical impacts include mortality, morbidity and injury rates, as well as economic losses. Very often these rates are directly related to safe housing. **For ethnic minorities, physical impact risks may include:** • Ethnic group members may live in housing that is structurally unsafe
Emergency response	The **emergency response** period occurs in the immediate aftermath of the disaster. **For ethnic minorities, post-impact risks may include:** • Cultural insensitivity of emergency personnel • Limited access of responders to victims • Lack of information • Immigration status as a barrier to seeking/receiving benefits • Language difficulties
Recovery	The **recovery** period refers to the first full year following a disaster. **For ethnic minorities, recovery phase risks may include:** • Lower incomes, lower savings account balances, greater unemployment, less property insurance, and less access to communication channels and information • Lack of health insurance • Difficulty accessing disaster services and navigating bureaucracies
Reconstruction	The **reconstruction** period follows recovery, extending several years beyond the disaster. Reconstruction surrounds a community's long-term restoration, including rebuilding, replacing infrastructure, obtaining loans, receiving assistance and locating permanent housing. **For ethnic minorities, reconstruction risks may include:** • Physical displacement • Stigmatization of the affected area • Decline in standards of living • Loss of community and jobs • Economic decline

Source: Fothergill et al., 1999

Summary

The psychosocial impact of disaster is best understood within an ecological model in which there are reverberating effects on the social, political and cultural fabric of the community. Psychological effects of trauma exposure are mediated though myriad contextual factors operating at individual, family, community and societal levels. The Disaster Ecology Model portrays the dynamic push and shove of these risk factors and resiliency factors that shape the child's experience of a disaster event. The single most powerful predictor of the child's psychological response to disaster is the intensity of exposure. The Population Exposure Model presents the wide-ranging nature of persons sustaining psychological impact: while relatively few persons experience extreme exposure, expanding rings of persons sustain moderate or even minimal impact. For persons living in poverty and those of race/ethnic minority status, excess risks for psychosocial consequences exist at every stage of the disaster life cycle.

Children's Psychological Responses to Disasters

Chapter 4

Children's Psychological Responses to Disasters

On successful completion of this chapter you should be able to:

1) Distinguish the spectrum of psychological responses to trauma
2) Describe the developmentally-related psychological responses to disaster for pre-school and school-age children and for adolescent youth
3) Differentiate acute and chronic stress responses for children exposed to disaster
4) Delineate the defining characteristics of acute stress disorder (ASD) and posttraumatic stress disorder (PTSD)
5) Enumerate factors that enhance resilience in children and adolescents

Key Concepts

- Depending upon the nature of the trauma, children may experience posttraumatic stress symptoms, grief and/or depression, anxiety symptoms or behavioral responses.
- Acute stress reactions are experienced by the majority of children exposed to disaster during impact and early post-impact phases while persistent, chronic stress reactions may be experienced by children who are subjected to an unceasing cascade of post-disaster adversities.
- For some children, psychological responses to disaster are sufficiently severe and distressing to meet criteria for a trauma-specific disorder such as acute stress disorder (ASD) or posttraumatic stress disorder (PTSD).
- Resilience is "mastery against adversity" and most children exhibit this capacity to overcome the challenges posed by disaster, restore equilibrium and even emerge stronger or transformed by the experience.

Introduction

One out of every four children experiences a significant traumatic event before reaching adulthood (Costello et al., 2002). The child's psychological response to trauma is fundamentally affected by the level of cognitive and emotional development. The child typically lives within a family system that is integrated into a community within a cultural and ethnic context. The child's responses to trauma are impacted by the psychological responses of parents, family members and citizens of the disaster-affected community.

Independent of the specific type of trauma, psychological responses tend to follow several common pathways (Table 4.1). Life threat and threat of physical harm may manifest as posttraumatic stress symptoms; loss may produce

reactions of grief and depression; persistent worries may cascade into anxiety; and ongoing life stressors may surface as behavioral problems (Pynoos & Nader, 1988).

Children with no previous psychiatric diagnosis may display anxiety and depressive symptoms, behavior problems and somatic symptoms in the aftermath of disaster. Children with pre-existing emotional and behavioral problems may experience exacerbation of symptoms following disaster, particularly when critical medications are in short supply, barriers to health care access arise, social support diminishes, and routines are disrupted. Children with physical illness may find that the post-disaster demands overwhelm their coping capacities. Some children experience traumatic bereavement following the disaster-related death of a parent or family member.

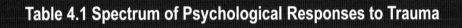

Table 4.1 Spectrum of Psychological Responses to Trauma

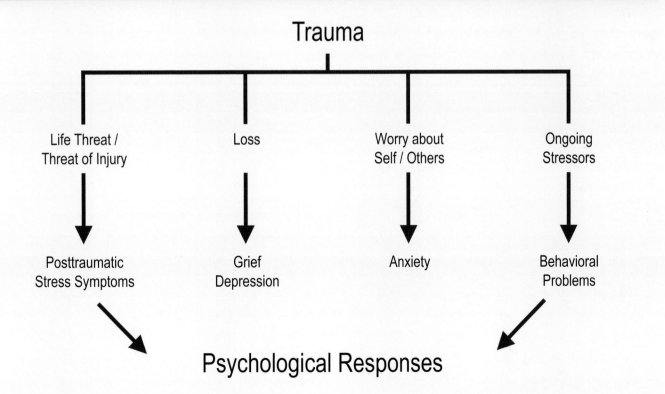

Source: Modified from Pynoos & Nader, 1988

Developmental Effects

The child's psychological response is determined and shaped by the nature of the stressors, the level of cognitive development, individual characteristics, childhood understanding of disaster causation, reactions of family members, and the effectiveness of the child's adaptive and coping mechanisms for regulating mood and controlling impulse.

Preschool Children

Preschool children are less likely to experience posttraumatic symptoms than older children (Bloch et al., 1956; Green et al., 1991). Younger children rely on parental and family figures to determine their perceived degree of risk or safety. Children resonate with parents' emotional states, attitudes and behaviors. As long as parents respond with some sense of equanimity, children feel protected and secure. Younger children have less specific cognitive awareness regarding the nature and meaning of the traumatic experience. Reactions of preschool children tend to be disorganized and agitated, manifested by generalized fears, separation anxiety, aggressive and disruptive behaviors, physical complaints, or loss of previously-mastered bowel and bladder control.

Level of cognitive development has a profound effect on the child's interpretation of, and psychological response to, the traumatic situation. Piaget (1967) observed that the child does not recognize the existence of chance happenings and believes that everything that happens is related to something they did or did not do. The trauma may be interpreted as a punishment for a self-perceived transgression. One child who was evacuated to a shelter because of extensive flooding in his home town believed the floods were a direct consequence of his repeatedly flushing the toilet at home, a behavior for which he had been reprimanded. A young girl believed that the Chowchilla bus kidnapping had occurred because she had called her mother "the meanest mother in the world" as she left for school that morning (Terr, 1981). A child in Miami thought that Hurricane Andrew had occurred because he hit his brother.

Younger children often have a skewed sense of time and have difficulty placing events in chronological order. Children may be prone to illusory experiences and cognitive distortions as they recount their traumatic situation. They may embellish or fabricate missing explanatory pieces from their own fears and wishes.

Terr (1988) noted that preschool children under three years of age have little capacity to verbally recall their traumatic experiences, although girls are generally more successful than boys. Younger children are more likely to reenact the trauma experience in their play activities and insert aspects of the disaster event into drawings or storytelling (Terr, 1981, 1991).

**Table 4.2
Psychological Responses in
Preschool Children**

- Sleep and appetite disturbances
- Fear of the dark
- Separation anxiety
- Nightmares
- Regressive behaviors
- Hypervigilence
- Behavioral reenactments
- Clinging/dependent behavior

School-age Children

The school-age child has a more mature cognitive understanding of the nature of the disaster event or traumatic situation, including potential threats of bodily injury and death. Symptoms following disaster exposure may include disturbance of regular sleep patterns, appetite change, behavior problems in school, decline in academic performance, disruptive behaviors, depression, anxiety disorders, somatic concerns, and PTSD symptoms. School-age children may experience secondary psychological symptoms as a consequence of their hyperarousal, agitation, anxiety or somatic symptoms.

Table 4.3
Psychological Responses in School-age Children

- Re-experiencing symptoms
- Disorganized or confused behaviors
- Somatic complaints
- Arousal symptoms
- Disruptive behaviors
- Anxiety symptoms
- Decreased academic performance

Adolescents

Post-traumatic stress symptoms become more like the adult pattern as children mature. The adolescent responds essentially as an adult with a similar range of symptoms and clinical presentations. However, the psychological response is often colored by the adolescent's awareness of a life unlived. Exposure to a perceived threat to life and safety may precipitate fear of a foreshortened future, accentuating the sense of biological fragility and increasing awareness of life's transience (Shaw, 2000). Adolescents exposed to disaster may fearfully avoid usually-enjoyed activities or alternatively, take flight into pleasure-seeking pursuits based on the sudden realization of life's potential brevity. This may lead to risk-taking or sensation-seeking behaviors and potential abuse of alcohol or other substances.

Table 4.4
Psychological Responses in Adolescents

- Anxiety
- Depression
- Guilt, anger, fear, disillusionment
- Fears of a foreshortened future
- Flight into pleasurable pursuits
- Substance abuse

Psychological Reactions to Disasters

1. Acute Stress Responses

The majority of persons exposed to a life-threatening experience will manifest acute stress symptoms. (Figure 4.1). During the disaster impact phase, children are at risk for physical harm from disaster hazards, and psychological distress from experiencing the terror of the event and witnessing harm to others. The majority of children and families experience a normal psychological response characterized by acute distress symptoms such as anxiety, fear and feelings of helplessness; grief and mourning in response to losses; mood symptoms associated with separation from friends and loved ones; behavior problems; and somatic ills. In most instances the stress symptoms dissipate as the child restores normal functioning, but some children may progress to a diagnosis of a psychiatric disorder.

Children and adolescents exposed to disasters exhibit acute stress responses in several domains of human functioning including changes in physiology, mood, thinking, behavior, and interpersonal relationships (Table 4.5).

Figure 4.1 Psychosocial Impact of Disasters

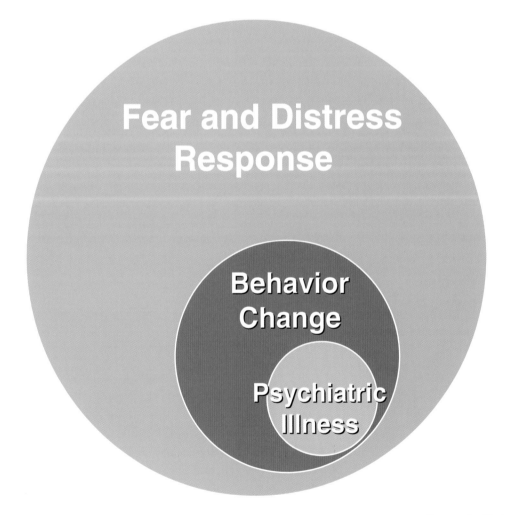

Source: Institute of Medicine, 2003

Table 4.5 Common Acute Stress Reactions in Children and Adolescents

Dimension	Common Acute Stress Reactions
Changes in bodily function	• Somatic complaints including headaches, stomach aches, rapid heartbeat, tightness in the chest • Sleep and appetite disturbances
Changes in behavior	• Disruptive behaviors, temper tantrums, agitation, hyperactivity • Clinging-dependent behaviors • Regressive behaviors: loss of toilet training, diminished language skills • Feelings of a foreshortened future, eagerness to live life to the fullest, flight into pleasure-seeking activities, substance abuse, conflicts with authorities • Avoidant and phobic symptoms
Changes in mood	• Specific fears that the disaster will recur • Feelings of insecurity, anxiety, fear, anger, sadness, depression and worries about the future • Anger • Irritability • Feelings of unfairness • Increased concerns regarding the safety of family members, friends and loved ones
Changes in thinking	• Child's distorted belief that he/she has caused the disaster • Loss of trust in the safety and security of the world • Loss of trust in adults' ability to protect children
Changes in interpersonal and social relationships	• Social withdrawal • Decreased motivation • Poor school performance

Following the destructive impact of a tornado striking Vicksburg, Mississippi, one-third of the children exhibited psychological reactions including anxiety, clinging-dependent behaviors, sleep disturbances, night terrors and regressive behaviors (Bloch et al., 1956). Shaw et al. (1995) found that 87 percent of school-age children in the direct path of Hurricane Andrew had moderate to severe posttraumatic stress symptoms (PTSS), and 57 percent had severe to very severe PTSS. The most common stress symptoms were sleep disturbances, nightmares, fears of recurrence, anxiety, and fears when thinking about the hurricane. Following the Buffalo Creek Disaster, most of the disaster-exposed children experienced emotional problems (Green et al., 1991). Preschool children evidenced trauma-specific fears and regressive behaviors but were generally less affected than older children and adolescents. Following the Indian Ocean tsunami, 14-38 percent of children, ages 8-14 years, experienced PTSS (Neuner et al., 2006). Prevalence and severity of symptoms were directly related to the intensity of traumatic exposure.

Terr (1981) described the psychological effects of human-generated violence on children. During the Chowchilla bus kidnapping, 23 children, ages 5-14 years, were held captive on a school bus for 27 hours. Following the episode, many of these children experienced traumatic nightmares (50 percent); fears of recurrence (85 percent); posttraumatic play involving themes of kidnapping (55 percent); and cognitive disturbances.

Following the Attack on America, September 11, 2001, a national survey found that 35 percent of children had one or more symptoms of stress and 47 percent were

concerned about their own safety (Schuster et al., 2001). Twenty-two percent of children in Manhattan were referred for counseling following the September 11 attack (Stuber et al., 2002).

2. Chronic Stress Responses

In the aftermath of disaster, a cascade of hardships and adversities ("secondary stressors") continues to impact the child and family. Post-disaster, exposure to chronic stressors may progressively erode the child's resiliency and increase the risk for psychological disorders and medical illnesses. Cumulative stress increases the risk for depression, suicidal thoughts, substance abuse, decreased social function, and aggressive and delinquent behaviors. Two years after the Buffalo Creek Disaster, one-third of children continued to meet diagnostic criteria for PTSD (Green et al., 1994). Remarkably, 17 years after the event, 7 percent still met diagnostic criteria for PTSD. In a study of child survivors of Hurricane Andrew, 70 percent of children still manifested moderate to severe PTSS during a follow-up assessment conducted 21 months after the storm (Shaw, 1996). McFarlane (1987) found that 26 months after exposure to a bushfire in Australia, one-third of the children were still preoccupied with the disaster and continued to exhibit significant emotional and behavioral problems.

The Project Liberty Counseling Service Utilization Study (Covell et al., 2006) indicated that in the 27 months following the September 11 attack, 9 percent of children received individual counseling. The most common emotional reactions were sadness, tearfulness, anger and irritability, sleep disturbances, and intrusive thoughts and images. Younger children were more likely to experience anxiety, problems in concentration, social isolation and withdrawal while older children (12-17 years) were more likely to exhibit numbing and avoidance reactions and to abuse substances.

Children who have been exposed to ongoing and repeated stressors such as child maltreatment and war-related trauma may evidence enduring psychological consequences (Table 4.6) Studies of children exposed to child maltreatment such as exposure to neglect, and emotional, physical or sexual abuse, have been found to have long-term changes in brain structure including decreased brain volume (De Bellis et al., 1999a,b; Cooper et al., 2007; Stover et al., 2007).

Depressive and grief symptoms frequently flow from the experiences of loss and change in disaster's aftermath. These symptoms may appear as changes in mood and manifest as feelings of sadness, tearfulness, irritability and hopelessness; loss of pleasure and interest in previously enjoyed activities; changes in behavior such as decreased school performance; changes in interpersonal and social relationships appearing as social avoidance, social withdrawal, isolation and interpersonal conflicts; changes in thinking such as decreased concentration, low self-esteem, diminished hope or preoccupation with suicide and death; negative expectations about the future; and changes in appetite and sleep patterns.

Anxiety symptoms are present to varying degrees in virtually all persons exposed to trauma. These symptoms appear in multiple forms: being afraid that the trauma could happen again; fears of dying or sustaining serious injury; worries about access to basic needs such as food, water, safety and security; fears for loved ones and family members in the absence of real threat; apprehension about the future; and somatic symptoms such as palpitations, difficulty breathing or gastrointestinal upset.

Behavioral symptoms may include hyperactivity, agitation, belligerence, truancy from school, and deterioration in academic performance. Children or adolescents may initiate or increase engagement in unhealthy behaviors such as cigarette smoking, alcohol or drug use, or excessive use of prescription medications.

Sleeper Effect: In some instances there may be a delayed psychological response to an acute trauma. This may occur when the maturing child acquires greater understanding of the consequences and ramifications of the traumatic experience that was not fully grasped at the time of the trauma. For example a young girl who was sexually abused may have initially perceived the assault as an aggressive attack, but later she may fully understand the assault as sexual with all its ramifications.

Table 4.6
Psychological Responses to Chronic Trauma

- Anxiety and mood disorders
- Dissociation
- Disruptive behaviors
- Loss and grief reactions
- Substance abuse
- Personality changes
- Suicidal behaviors
- Psychiatric comorbidity
- Somatic ills
- Central nervous system changes

3. Psychopathology

In some cases the psychological responses to disaster are of sufficient magnitude to meet diagnostic criteria for a trauma-specific syndrome such as an acute stress disorder (ASD) or posttraumatic stress disorder (PTSD).

"Dissociation" symptoms are important in the diagnosis of ASD and require brief description prior to presenting the diagnostic criteria for these syndromes:

"Dissociation" describes the disconnection or lack of connection between things usually associated with each other (ISSTD, 2007). Usually the functions of consciousness, memory, identity and perception are integrated and interconnected but dissociation implies a separation among these functions. For example, with "emotional numbing", a person may think about an event that was extremely upsetting yet have no feelings about it – thinking and feeling are disconnected. "Depersonalization" is the sense of being detached from and "not in" one's body, sometimes described as an "out-of-body" experience. "Derealization" is the sense of the world not being real. Some persons have the sensation of "watching" the world as they would watch a movie. "Dissociative amnesia" refers to the inability to recall important personal information that goes well beyond ordinary forgetfulness. Disaster survivors may lack recall of major portions of the traumatic episode despite retaining consciousness during the disaster event.

Acute stress disorder (ASD): ASD is diagnosed when an individual develops anxiety, dissociative and related symptoms within one month after exposure to an extreme traumatic stressor (DSM-IV, 1994).

This disturbance usually lasts for at least two days and does not persist beyond four weeks. Either while experiencing the traumatic event or after the event, the individual has at least three of the following dissociative symptoms: a subjective sense of numbing, detachment, or absence of emotional responsiveness; a reduction in awareness of his/her surroundings; derealization; depersonalization; or dissociative amnesia. Furthermore, following the trauma, the traumatic event is persistently re-experienced and relived with intrusive images, dreams, thoughts and perceptions. The individual may consciously avoid any reminders that may arouse recollections of the trauma. In order to meet ASD clinical criteria, these symptoms must cause clinically significant distress, interfere with normal functioning, or impair the individual's ability to pursue necessary tasks. Finally, to qualify as ASD, the individual must experience at least one symptom from each of the three PTSD symptom clusters: 1) "hyperraousal" (difficulty sleeping, irritability, poor concentration, hypervigilance, exaggerated startle response, motor restlessness), 2) re-experiencing, and 3) avoidance.

Meiser-Stredman et al. (2007) studied 367 child survivors of motor vehicle crashes, ages 6-17 years, and found that only 9 percent met diagnostic criteria for ASD. However, twice as many met "subsyndromal criteria" because of the inability to fully document the dissociative symptoms. The authors conclude that the "excessively strict" dissociative criteria for youth makes ASD a rare diagnosis in children, typically reserved for those who been exposed to sudden, unexpected, brutal violence. Therefore, most children who do develop PTSD are not diagnosed with ASD in the month following trauma exposure (Stover et al., 2007).

Table 4.7
Acute Stress Disorder

A   The person has been exposed to a traumatic event in which both of the following were present:
1. The person experienced, witnessed, or was confronted with an event or events that involved actual or threatened death or serious injury or a threat to the physical integrity of self or others
2. The person's response involved intense fear, helplessness or horror

Note: In children, this may be expressed instead by disorganized or agitated behavior

B   Either while experiencing or after experiencing the distressing event, the individual has three (or more) of the following dissociative symptoms:
1. a subjective sense of numbing, detachment, or absence of emotional responsiveness
2. a reduction in awareness of his or her surroundings (e.g., "being in a daze")
3. derealization
4. depersonalization
5. dissociative amnesia (inability to recall an important aspect of the trauma)

C   The traumatic event is persistently reexperienced in at least one of the following ways:
1. recurrent images thoughts, dreams, illusions, or flashbacks
2. a sense of reliving the experience
3. distress on exposure to reminders of the traumatic event

D   Marked avoidance of stimuli that arouse recollections of the trauma (thoughts, feelings, conversations, activities, places, people)

E   Marked symptoms of anxiety or increased arousal (difficulty sleeping, irritability, poor concentration, hypervigilance, exaggerated startle response, motor restlessness)

F   The disturbance causes clinically significant distress or impairment.

G   The disturbance lasts for a minimum of 2 days and a maximum of 4 weeks and occurs within 4 weeks of the traumatic event.

Posttraumatic stress disorder (PTSD): The lifetime prevalence of exposure to a traumatic event in which the individual is confronted with a real or imagined threat of physical injury or death is estimated at 70 percent for men and 50 percent for women (Kessler et al., 1995). Among those exposed to severe trauma, approximately 10 percent will meet threshold clinical criteria for PTSD, with twice as many women as men being so affected. Naturalistic studies indicate that men recover faster than women. Even five years post-trauma, approximately one-third of adults with PTSD continue to meet diagnostic criteria (Breslau et al., 1998).

The predominant manifestations of PTSD are a compelling need to relive, re-experience and repeat the traumatic experience, paradoxically oscillating with a need to avoid any thoughts, feelings, perceptions or situations that remind one of the traumatic event (APA, 1994). Individuals are likely to vacillate between denial and a flooding of consciousness with intrusive images, thoughts and perceptions with their associated effects of fear, terror and helplessness. PTSD diagnosis should be considered for individuals whose symptoms persist for longer than one month.

A study of a representative sample of adults in Manhattan, 5-8 weeks after September 11, revealed that 19 percent reported a current history of PTSD, equivalent to twice the rate of PTSD prior to the attacks (Galea et al., 2002). Fifty-eight percent of respondents reported at least one PTSD symptom. A diagnosis of PTSD was predicted by exposure to two or more stressors in the prior twelve months, a panic attack during or shortly after the attack, lack of social support, direct involvement in rescue efforts and loss of personal possessions due to the attacks. The most common PTSD symptoms were intrusive memories (27 percent), insomnia (25 percent) and exaggerated startle reactions (24 percent).

Interviews of 516 men and 493 women in New York City, conducted 3-6 months after September 11, revealed that 56 percent had at least one severe, or two or more mild-to-moderate, posttraumatic stress symptoms, but only 27 percent sought treatment (De Lisi et al., 2003). Among study participants, 29 percent had changed employment, 10 percent had lost a close family member or friend and one-third reported painful memories triggered by traumatic reminders (De Lisi et al., 2003).

It has been estimated that 25-45 percent of children will be exposed to a traumatic event and among those exposed, 5-45 percent will develop PTSD (Stover et al., 2007). Only a few community-based studies of PTSD in the child and adolescent population have been published. Baseline rates of PTSD are approximately 3-6 percent in school-age children and 0.1 percent in preschool children (Reinherz et al., 1993; Scheeringa et al., 2003). A national survey of adolescents, ages 12-17 years, found that 4 percent of boys and 6 percent of girls met diagnostic criteria for PTSD (Kilpatrick et al., 2003). Copeland et al. (2007) found that two-thirds of children in the Great Smoky Mountain Study reported at least one traumatic event before the age of

16 years and 14 percent had experienced one or more posttraumatic stress symptoms.

Researchers recommend that the criteria for PTSD in the preschool age child be modified to be more sensitive to regressive behaviors or child-specific biological measures that differ from those of adults, such as heart rate, frequency of smiling and vocalizations (Stoddard et al., 2006).

Guinea: Kouankan refugee camp
2006 © EC/ECHO/Pierre Christophe Chatzisavas

Table 4.8 Posttraumatic Stress Disorder

Criteria for diagnosis of PTSD	Manifest as:
A Exposure to a traumatic event	• The individual experiences, witnesses or is confronted with an event or events that involve actual or threatened death, serious injury or a threat to the physical integrity of self or others • The response is associated with intense fear, helplessness and horror • Children: Disorganized/agitated behavior

B Re-experiencing of the traumatic event. The traumatic event can be a dominating psychological experience that retains its power to evoke panic, terror, dread, grief, or despair. Trauma-related stimuli that trigger recollections of the original event may have the power to evoke mental images, emotional responses, and psychological reactions associated with the trauma. For diagnosis, at least 2 re-experiencing symptoms must be present.	• Recurrent images, thoughts, perceptions
	• Recurrent distressing dreams
	• Daytime fantasies
	• Flashbacks
	• Psychological distress when exposed to traumatic reminders
	• Reliving of the traumatic experience. Acting or feeling as if the events were recurring
	• Children:
	  - May have dreams without recognizable content
	  - Reenactment of the trauma can be observed in repetitive play, drawings, or verbalizations
	  - Behavioral reenactments of the trauma such as a boy with an axe who says he is a hurricane
	  - Symbolic representation of the trauma that compulsively repeats some aspect of the trauma (e.g. creating a play village destroyed by a hurricane)
	  - Play does not usually relieve anxiety
	  - Frightening dreams without recognizable content

C Avoidance of reactions elicited by stimuli associated to the traumatic event. These symptoms reflect behavioral, cognitive, or emotional strategies that individuals use in an attempt to reduce the likelihood they will expose themselves to trauma-related stimuli. These strategies are used in an attempt to minimize the intensity of their psychological response if they are exposed to such stimuli. For diagnosis, at least 3 avoidance symptoms must be present.	• Avoid thoughts, feelings, conversation
	• Avoid activities, places or people that arouse memories of the traumatic event
	• Inability to recall aspects of trauma
	• Decreased interest in significant activities
	• Feelings of detachment/estrangement from others
	• Decreased range of affect
	• Sense of foreshortened future
	• Children:
	  - Avoid internal or external cues that serve as traumatic reminders
	  - Avoid play or school activities, electronic media representations (TV, video games, music, etc.) that remind one of the traumatic experience

D Increased arousal. For diagnosis, at least 2 arousal symptoms must be present.	• Insomnia • Irritability • Difficulty concentrating • Hyper-vigilance • Exaggerated startle response
E Duration of symptoms at least more than one month	• Acute: symptoms less then 3 months • Chronic: more than 3 months • Delayed onset: symptoms start at least 6 months after event
F Significant social, occupational, or other distress as a result of these symptoms.	• Problems at work • Difficulty adhering to rules and daily activities

Source: APA, 1994; MSF, 2005

Children: Stress, Trauma and Disasters

Table 4.9
Alternative PTSD Criteria for Preschool Children

A   The person has been exposed to a traumatic event:
1. The person experienced, witnessed, or was confronted with an event or events that involved actual or threatened death or serious injury or a threat to the physical integrity of self or others
2. Is not required because preverbal children cannot report on their reaction at the time of the event and an adult may not have been present to witness the child's reaction.

B   The traumatic event is persistently re-experienced in one (or more) of the following ways:
1. Recurrent and intrusive recollection of the event (but not necessarily distressing), including images, thoughts, or perceptions. Note: In young children, repetitive play may occur in which themes or aspects of the trauma are expressed.
2. Recurrent distressing dreams of the event. Note: In children, there may be frightening dreams without recognizable content.
3. Objective, behavioral manifestations of a flashback are observed but the individual may not be able to verbalize the content of the experience.
4. Intense psychological distress at exposure to internal or external cues that symbolize or resemble an aspect of the traumatic event.

C   Persistent avoidance of stimuli associated with the trauma and numbing of general responsiveness (not present before the trauma), as indicated by one (or more) of the following:
1. Efforts to avoid activities, places, or people that arouse recollections of the trauma
2. Markedly diminished interest or participation in significant activities. Note: In young children, this is mainly observed as constriction of play.
3. Feeling of detachment or estrangement from others. Note: In young children, this is mainly observed as social withdrawal.
4. Restricted range of emotions (for example, unable to have loving feelings)

D   Persistent symptoms of increased arousal (not present before the trauma), as indicated by one (or more) of the following:
1. Difficulty falling or staying asleep
2. Irritability or outbursts of anger or extreme temper tantrums and fussiness
3. Difficulty concentrating
4. Hypervigilance
5. Exaggerated startle response

Usually a child or adolescent who meets diagnostic criteria for a posttraumatic stress disorder will manifest other psychological and psychiatric problems. The most common co-existing psychiatric disorders are mood disorders such as major depression, and dysthymia (chronically depressed mood lasting longer than one year); anxiety disorders such as separation anxiety disorder, generalized anxiety disorder and/or specific phobias; behavior problems such as attention deficit hyperactivity disorder (ADHD), oppositional defiant disorder (ODD) or conduct disorder (CD), substance abuse and various physical complaints.

Two years after the Buffalo Creek disaster, 30 percent of children less than 8 years of age and 39 percent of children older than 8 years met criteria for PTSD (Green et al., 1991). According to a survey of 8,266 New York

City children in grades 4-12, the rate of PTSD increased from 2 to 10 percent following September 11, and the rate of separation anxiety disorder doubled (Fremont, 2004). Children who developed PTSD and other less severe psychological responses continued to manifest ongoing psychological difficulties long after the terrorist event. Research suggests that 30 to 50 percent of the children exposed to a terrorist act experience one or more of the following: PTSD, anxiety disorders, somatic ills, mood disorders and disturbances in development and behavior.

Mood Disorders: Depressive symptoms occur in 10-40 percent of those exposed to trauma. Approximately seventy-five percent of adults with PTSD have co-existing psychiatric diagnoses, with 35-45 percent having a lifetime history of depression (Breslau et al., 1998). A recent study noted that 18 percent of adolescents manifested a major mood disorder following exposure to a cyclone (Kar & Bastia, 2006).

Mood symptoms in children are comparable to those experienced by adults, with some exceptions. For example, younger children frequently display regressive clinging-dependent behaviors and somatic symptoms, while adolescents are more likely to engage in suicidal thoughts or actions and to increase substance abuse behaviors. The most common symptoms in children and adolescents are changes in mood such as feelings of sadness, tearfulness, depression and irritability; behavior changes such as poor school performance and loss of interest in previously enjoyed activities; disturbance in relationships such as social avoidance, interpersonal and family conflicts; somatic ills; and disturbances in thinking such as low self-esteem, self-deprecation, feelings of hopelessness, inability to concentrate and suicidal ideation.

Table 4.10 Symptoms of Depression

Changes in Mood	• Feelings of sadness and depression • Irritability • Loss of interest in pleasurable activities
Changes in Behavior	• Changes in personality • Changes in school performance • Loss of interest in previously enjoyed activities • Tearfulness • Impaired functioning
Changes in Relationship	• Social avoidance • Social withdrawal/ isolation • Interpersonal conflicts • Family conflicts
Changes in Thinking	• Low self-esteem • Self-deprecation • Self-absorbed • Feelings of hopelessness and helplessness • Demoralization • Inability to think or concentrate • Preoccupation with death/suicide • Negative expectations about the future
Changes in Bodily Functioning	• Change in appetite and body weight • Change in sleep pattern • Change in activity level • Somatic complaints

Disruptive Behavior Disorders: Children (primarily boys) exposed to traumatic events may demonstrate disturbances in behavior such as hyperactivity, belligerence, and conduct disturbances. Adolescents may increase substance use and abuse. Immediately post-impact, there may be a temporary decrease in school-based disruptive behaviors as noted by Shaw et al. (1995) for child survivors of Hurricane Andrew.

4. Resilience

Resilience is a measure of the individual's capacity to rapidly restore pre-disaster levels of function and psychological equilibrium. Rutter (1985) noted that children with good coping skills, self-mastery, easy temperament, and a history of a good relationship with an adult were more resistant and less vulnerable to psychopathology in later life. Garmezy et al. (1984) and Werner and Smith (1982) stressed the importance of early family relationships, self-efficacy, and an inner conviction that one's life is within one's control as factors contributing to resiliency.

Resilience has been defined as "the capacity to deal with, overcome, be strengthened by, and even transformed by experiences of adversity, including both human-generated and natural disasters" (Henderson, 2001). Factors that enhance child resiliency are effective parenting, positive self-concept, self-regulation, social competence, cognitive flexibility, adaptability to new situations, problem-solving skills, ease with transitions, communication skills, empathy, assertiveness in one's self-interest, humor, religious affiliation, and the ability to elicit caretaking behaviors (Masten, 2007).

Masten (2007) emphasizes that early attachments and healthy caregiver relationships that provide emotional security facilitate prosocial behaviors, tolerance for frustration, effective information processing, self-regulation, stress management, and adaptability. She recognizes the important influences of the school and community in fostering the child's socialization and providing opportunities for mastery and learning. Integral to resiliency are the child's accrued "competencies" including elements of academic, social, interpersonal, and phase-specific mastery (Masten, 2007).

Intrinsic to resiliency is the role of genetics, neurotransmitters, and stress response systems. Some individuals appear to release higher levels of "neuropeptide Y" and allopregnanolone (a product of the adrenal glands) in response to stress; reactions that appear to confer natural resiliency and to diminish anxiety (Hoge et al., 2007). In contrast, children who sustain prolonged exposure to poor parenting and nurturance may experience detrimental neurobiological and neurohormonal changes (such as decreased levels of oxytocin, a neurohomone believed to facilitate emotional bonding to others), thereby compromising social relatedness (Cooper, 2007; Hoge et al., 2007). Conversely, there is evidence that a short form of the serotonin transporter gene may be associated with decreased resiliency and increased risk for depression (Gunnar, 2007).

Table 4.11
Factors that Enhance Resilience in Children and Adolescence

Individual protective factors
- The capacity to recognize opportunities in adversity
- Ability to elaborate problem-solving and emotional coping skills
- Good social skills with peers and adults
- Personal awareness of strengths and limitations
- Feelings of empathy for others
- Internal locus of control - a belief that one's efforts can make a difference
- Sense of humor
- Positive self-concept
- Self-reliance
- Cognitive flexibility
- Positive emotions (optimism, sense of humor, interests, joy)
- Ability to interact positively with others
- Active coping
- Physical exercise
- Religion

Family protective factors
- Positive family ambience
- Good parent-child relationships
- Parental harmony
- A valued social role in the household, such as helping siblings or doing household chores

Community protective factors
- Strong social support networks
- Supportive extended family
- A close relationship with unrelated mentor
- Good peer relationships
- Community influences that offer positive role models
- Positive school experiences
- Valued social role such as a job, volunteering or helping neighbors
- Membership in a religious or faith community
- Extra-curricular activities

Source: Newman and Blackburn, 2002 ; Cooper et al., 2007

Summary

For children, psychological responses to disaster exposure vary based on the nature of the trauma. Disaster-exposed children may display acute and chronic stress reactions, posttraumatic stress symptoms, grief, depression, anxiety symptoms or behavior changes. The child's level of cognitive and emotional development interplays with the type and intensity of exposure to shape the child's psychological responses to disaster. During the impact phase and early aftermath, acute stress reactions are experienced by the majority of children exposed to disaster. For those children who are subjected to an unabated bombardment of post-disaster hardships, chronic stress reactions may be prominent. For some children, psychological responses to disaster are sufficiently severe and distressing to meet criteria for a trauma-specific disorder such as acute stress disorder (ASD) or posttraumatic stress disorder (PTSD). Nevertheless, the most common outcome for both children and adults who survive a disaster is resilience, defined as "mastery against adversity." Children frequently overcome the challenges posed by disaster and emerge stronger and positively transformed by the experience.

Children with Special Needs During Disasters

Chapter 5

Children with Special Needs During Disasters

On successful completion of this chapter you should be able to:

1) Apply the concept of special needs populations to children and adolescents
2) Identify stressors that affect children with special needs during disasters
3) Identify strategies to support children with special needs during disasters

Key Concepts

- Children with special needs include the psychiatrically and medically ill, those who have suffered from multiple episodes of child maltreatment from parents and caretakers, the developmentally disabled, children in foster care and children who are disadvantaged by poverty.
- During disasters and extreme events, children with special needs may have diminished resiliency and fewer resources to manage disaster adversities, leading to heightened risk for psychological disorders.
- Special needs children should be prioritized in disaster planning.
- Children with special needs require customized interventions to optimize their safety and protection during disasters.

Source: FEMA photolibrary

Introduction

Special populations are defined as "groups of people whose needs may require additional, customized, or specialized approaches in preparedness for, response to, and recovery from extreme events" (Flynn, 2006). Children with special needs include those who have been exposed to multiple and repetitive psychosocial adversities before, during, and after disaster impact.

When children encounter interpersonal violence; live in poverty; or experience severe medical illness, developmental disabilities or psychiatric disorders; their psychological vulnerability to future traumatic events is increased (Balaban, 2006). In consequence, special needs children include: children who have suffered maltreatment, children with developmental disabilities, children with special psychiatric needs, children with special medical needs, children living in foster care, children living in poverty and children with limited language proficiency (Table 5.1).

Table 5.1
Children with Special Needs

Children who have been exposed to maltreatment
- Physical abuse
- Emotional abuse
- Neglect
- Sexual abuse

Children with developmental disabilities
- Blind and visually impaired
- Deaf and hard of hearing
- Mobility impaired
- Mentally ill
- Brain disorders and injuries
- Chronically ill
- Drug and/or alcohol dependent
- Dually-diagnosed with mental illness and substance abuse

Children with special psychiatric needs
- Children who were previously defined as psychiatrically disturbed, and/or who were receiving psychotropic medication, and/or whose condition worsened due to the lack of access to medications
- Children with preexisting psychosocial and psychiatric problems which are exacerbated by the stress of disaster

Children who experience cultural/ethnic health disparities or live in geographic isolation
- Cultural/ethnic groups
- Rural residents

Children with limited language proficiency
- Limited-English or non-English speaking
- Refugees
- Legal immigrants
- Illegal/undocumented immigrants
- Sign language

Children who live in economic disadvantage
- Population-wide poverty
- Living at or below the poverty line
- Working poor

Children with special medical needs
- Children with medical trauma
- Children with medical needs
- Families with children with medical needs

Others
- Juvenile offenders
- Dependent on public transportation
- Families underserved by public health
- Sheltered juveniles: runaways, battered youth
- Homeless youth

Source: American Psychiatric Association, 2007

Children Exposed To Maltreatment

Complex Trauma

Complex trauma derives from repetitive and cumulative exposure to traumatic episodes. Applied to children, complex trauma refers to exposure to violence which begins in childhood and is repeated throughout the developmental years. The consequences of complex trauma exposure-- emotional crisis, loss of a safe base, loss of direction, and inability to detect or respond to danger cues-- increase the child's vulnerability to future trauma. In complex trauma, the child is exposed to dangers that are unpredictable and uncontrollable; the child's resources are redirected toward survival rather than growth and development. Children who experience complex trauma are particularly susceptible to the "add on" of traumatic experience associated with disaster.

Source: NCTSN, 2003

Child maltreatment is a complex trauma experienced within a family or care-giving environment in which a child is exposed to multiple episodes of physical, emotional, and verbal abuse, and possibly sexual abuse. Extending into adulthood, abused individuals suffer from the enduring effects of childhood traumatic experiences. Child maltreatment is a risk factor for disruptive behaviors, mood and anxiety disorders, and posttraumatic stress disorder (Mcleer et al., 1994). Annually in the United States, three million reports of child maltreatment are processed by child protective services and one million are definitively documented and confirmed (1.3 percent of the pediatric population) (Kaufman, 2007). A global estimate indicates that 133-275 million children worlwide are exposed to domestic violence (UNICEF, 2006). For the United States, estimates range from 339,000 to 2.7 million.

Table 5.2
Child Maltreatment

Physical abuse: Non-accidental physical harm or injury to a child resulting in physical injuries (ranging from minimal to fatal) inflicted by persons caring for them. Acts of violence include, but are not limited to: slapping, shaking, punching, hitting, kicking, and burning the child.

Emotional abuse: Habitual patterns of verbal abuse and related behaviors characterized by the caretaker demeaning, belittling, tormenting, and denigrating the child's feelings of self-worth and confidence.

Psychological abuse: Actions causing psychological distress including social isolation, intimidation, degradation, humiliation, false accusations, ignoring and dismissing the child's needs.

Neglect: Willful failure to provide adequate care and protection for children. Neglect may take many forms such as physical, emotional and educational neglect manifested by failure to arrange for appropriate care, custody and supervision. Neglect may involve such deprivations as not providing food, clothing, or appropriate medical treatments; exposing children to dangerous environments; or keeping children from school.

Sexual abuse: Sexual exploitation of children and/or the erotization of children. Sexual abuse refers to any sexual behaviors which occur without consent, without equality or as a result of coercion. Sexual aggression invariably involves the use of threat, intimidation, exploitation of authority, or force with the aim of imposing one's sexual will on a non-consenting person for the purpose of sexual gratification.

Exposure to violence in the home is frequently multi-generational. Predictors of maltreatment include weak family bonding, ineffective parenting, inadequate parental supervision and monitoring, exposure to violence and reinforcement of coercive behaviors in the home.

Although high-profile school shootings are rare and extreme events, youth-on-youth violence is prevalent among school-age youth, with physical fighting and bullying behavior reported by 30-40 percent of students (Olweus, 1997; Nansel et al., 2001). Bullying is defined as the intentional, repeated production of physical and/or psychological injury or discomfort upon another person who is unable to defend him/herself. Boys are more likely to self-report engaging in physical bullying activities and to be the victims of physical violence. Girls are more likely to report being victimized by social exclusion, gossip and

sexual comments. The most common type of bullying involves verbal bullying such as name-calling, taunting, teasing or rumor-mongering.

A survey of 1,100 school students demonstrated that those exposed to violence are at increased risk for psychiatric disorders (Schwab-Stone et al., 1995). Child victims of complex trauma may exhibit impairment in one or multiple domains (Table 5.3). Children who experience maltreatment at home, in school or in their neighborhoods are more vulnerable to the psychosocial consequences of subsequent trauma exposure, including disaster, due to the cumulative effects of trauma exposure, loss of resiliency, diminished self-efficacy and lack of psychological support from caregivers.

Table 5.3
Domains of Impairment in Children Exposed to Complex Trauma

I. Attachment
- Uncertainty about the reliability and predictability of the world
- Problems with boundaries
- Distrust and suspiciousness
- Social isolation
- Interpersonal difficulties

II. Biology
- Increased medical problems
- Problems with coordination, balance, muscle tone
- Hypersensitivity to physical contact
- Somatization—bodily symptoms

III. Emotional Regulation
- Difficulty with emotional self-regulation
- Difficulty describing feelings
- Difficulty communicating wishes and desires

IV. Dissociation
- Distinct alterations in states of consciousness
- Amnesia—loss of memory for selective events
- Depersonalization and derealization

V. Behavioral Control
- Difficulty understanding and complying with rules
- Poor modulation of impulses
- Self-destructive behavior
- Aggression against others
- Sleep disturbances
- Eating disorders
- Substance abuse
- Communication of traumatic past by reenactment in day-to-day behavior or play

VI. Cognition
- Learning difficulties
- Problems with language development
- Difficulties in attention regulation and executive functioning
- Difficulty planning and anticipating

VII. Self-Concept
- Lack of a continuous, predictable sense of self
- Low self-esteem
- Shame and guilt

Source: NCTSN, 2003

Children in Foster Care

The United State welfare system subsumes a complex matrix of services and programs which vary by state and across communities (Grigsby, 2002). Children who are placed in foster care have usually experienced neglect and physical, emotional and/or sexual abuse. These children have frequently experienced a myriad of stressors within the family including mental disorders, substance abuse, domestic violence, financial hardships, chronic medical illness, and death of loved ones. Environmental stressors may include racial and ethnic discrimination, unemployment and poverty.

The foster care population is estimated to number about 500,000, with children residing in a variety of settings such as youth shelters, group homes, domestic violence shelters, residential treatment centers and foster homes. Children in foster care have higher rates of child maltreatment and psychiatric disorders. The high prevalence of previous trauma increases the vulnerability and diminishes the resilience of foster children when they are subsequently exposed to disasters and extreme events.

Hurricane Katrina brought the vulnerabilities of foster care children into sharp focus. Many of the 13,000 children who were in foster care in Louisiana, Alabama and Mississippi prior to storm impact were displaced after the storm. The foster children of Katrina frequently experienced separations from adult caretakers and the other foster care children with whom they were living at the time of storm impact. Displacement and relocation of foster children disrupted their schooling and friendship networks. Those who were resettled to other states often lost their eligibility to receive the welfare and Medicaid benefits from their state of origin (Gelles, 2006).

Children with Developmental Disabilities

Developmental disability is defined as physical or mental disability, or a combination of both, that is continuous and manifest during childhood. Developmental disability is frequently evidenced by limitations in expressive and receptive language, self-care, learning, mobility, and capacity for independent living. The population prevalence of developmental disability is 2-3 percent. Developmental disabilities may derive from a diversity of origins: congenital malformations; birth injuries; brain injuries; and chronic medical illnesses such as cystic fibrosis, HIV infection, diabetes, and neurological disabilities.

Developmentally-disabled children are at elevated risk for child maltreatment, physical abuse and sexual abuse. Children with disabilities are two to ten times more likely to be sexually abused and twice as likely to be physically abused compared with children who have no disabilities (Westat Inc., 1993).

Disability and abuse interrelate in a vicious cycle. Children with developmental disabilities are more likely to be abused. Abuse, in turn, precipitates further developmental delays across social, psychological, physical and cognitive domains. Worsening developmental problems exacerbate the risk for further abuse. Ongoing and repetitive episodes of trauma sustained by children with developmental disabilities significantly increase their vulnerability when they confront a natural or human-generated disaster.

Children with Special Medical Needs

Medical illness and medical procedures are associated with emotional distress, anxiety, feelings of helplessness, physical pain and fears of threat to life--powerful traumatic stressors for children. Moreover, these stressors reverberate throughout the child's family, straining coping capacities and draining financial resources.

Approximately 5 percent of children are hospitalized for an acute or chronic illness, injury or disability. One thousand children receive organ transplants each year. One-in-five children admitted to a pediatric intensive care unit will develop PTSD within six months following discharge.

Annually, in the United States, between 9,000 and 12,000 children are newly diagnosed with cancer (Zebrack, 2007). Cancer is the second leading cause of death for children, ages 1-14 years. There are more than 250,000 child cancer survivors in the United States. Parents of adolescents with cancer have a 35-45 percent chance of developing PTSD, a higher rate than that experienced by the child cancer victims (Kazak et al., 2004).

The care of children with acute and chronic medical conditions represents a serious challenge for those planning and preparing for disaster. Children with special medical needs are often biologically stressed, less resilient and more vulnerable to the added impact of disaster stressors. In the aftermath of Hurricane Katrina there was a catastrophic loss of hospitals, community and private medical offices, pharmacies, patient information systems, and health insurance coverage. Children with acute and chronic medical conditions were precipitously deprived of medical support services. Many families sought emergency care to obtain life-sustaining medications for their children with medical conditions such as asthma, diabetes, and renal disease requiring regular dialysis. The St. Jude Children's Research Hospital website documented the disruption of live-sustaining cancer treatments for 170 pediatric patients due to the closure and evacuation of Gulf Coast hospitals. A significant portion of the pediatric inpatient population in New Orleans experienced the rigors of evacuation to specialized pediatric health care facilities outside the storm-damaged area.

Recommendations for disaster preparedness for parents with medically ill children are presented in the Table 5.4.

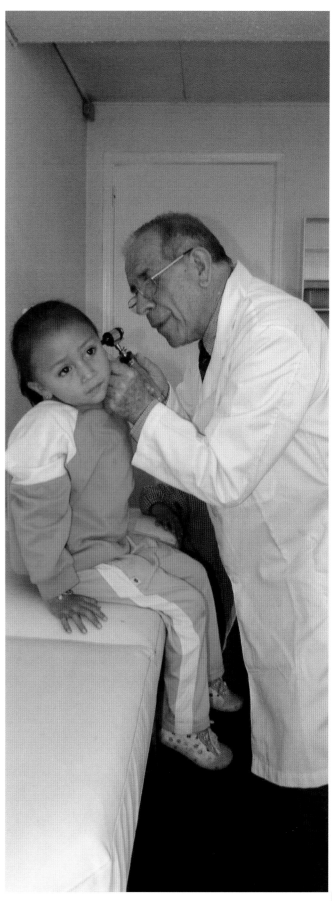

Children with Special Psychiatric Needs

Disasters have greater impact on families where a family member has a psychiatric or substance abuse diagnoses. One out of every five adults will have a diagnosable mental disorder or substance abuse problem. There are approximately 11 million children with a parent who is alcohol dependent. Children who suffer the consequences of parental psychopathology often have significant emotional and behavioral problems.

As a further complication, there is evidence of increasing fragmentation of the American family. The birth rate among unmarried women has increased by fifty percent between 1980 and 1990 (Gilliam et al., 2007). One out of every four children lives in a single parent family (and among African American families, the rate is one-in-two). Half of all marriages result in divorce.

According to the 1999 Surgeon General's Report, 21 percent of United States children, ages 9-17 years, have a diagnosable mental or addictive disorder. Furthermore, 5-6 percent of youth have a mental disorder that significantly impairs school performance, social functioning and abilities to meet the demands of everyday life (DHHS, 1999). There is evidence of an increase in pervasive developmental disorders characterized by developmental delays coupled with impairments in language, communication and social skills. Severe mental disorders, such as autism, childhood-onset schizophrenia, mood and anxiety disorders, obsessive compulsive disorders, Tourette's, attention deficit disorders and severe behavior control problems often require ongoing psychopharmacological interventions. The encounter with disaster may disrupt the family system which is already challenged to maintain effective support and essential therapy for children with psychiatric needs.

Table 5.4
Recommendations for Caregivers of Children with Special Health Needs

- Have a clearly defined disaster care plan for child.
- Develop strong alliances with health care providers.
- Maintain phone numbers of health providers.
- Know the location of emergency health centers.
- Have a medical supplies kit tailored to the needs of the child.
- Obtain medical identification tags for your child.
- Train family members to assume the role of in-home health care providers.
- Identify a common point of contact (neighbor, friend, or relative) in the event that family members are separated.
- Identify an out-of-state contact person in the event that local communications are disrupted.
- Stockpile foods that are essential for special dietary needs or restrictions.
- Learn the disaster plan at the child's school, including how the school plans to reunite children and families if a disaster strikes during school hours.
- Know where evacuation shelters are located.
- Learn the community's evacuation routes.
- For children with medical conditions requiring. electrical power, notify utility companies to provide emergency support during a disaster.
- Identify shelters in the area that provide continuous power during disasters.
- Create contingency plans should the utility company not be able to provide alternative sources of power in the event of power loss.
- Evacuate when told to do so.

Source: Adapted from Markenson and Reynolds, 2006

Poverty, Ethnicity and Culture

Poverty:

Children living in poverty represent a special population with elevated risks for psychological consequences following trauma exposure due to limited resources compounded with ongoing financial and household stressors. Poverty, with its associated child-specific stressors, poor prenatal care, low birth weight, malnutrition, environmental stressors, and feelings of powerlessness, is a risk factor for mental disorders. Poor families lack transportation, adequate housing, access to health care, and money to spend on health-promoting activities.

The National Center for Children in Poverty reports that 13 million children live in poverty (less that $20,000 for a family of four). This translates to approximately 19 percent of all children under 18 years of age (Gilliam et al., 2007). Several race/ethnic minorities are over-represented among the impoverished with poverty rates estimated at 35 percent for African-Americans, 28 percent for Latinos, and 29 percent for American Indians (National Center for Children in Poverty, 2006). In contrast, the poverty rate is lowest for Asian Americans at 11 percent.

Children living in poverty frequently live in housing that offers minimal protection in times of disaster. For example, at the time of Hurricane Katrina, 13 percent of children in Louisiana lived in "extreme poverty" (defined as household income that is below half of the federal poverty level, or $9,675 for a family of four). These families lived in decrepit housing in flood zones with no dependable transportation and thus no way to evacuate.

Culture/Ethnicity:

The United States is a multicultural society with a race/ethnic composition of 68.4 percent White/non-Hispanic, 14.2 percent Hispanic/Latino, 12.2 percent Black/non-Hispanic, 4.2 percent Asian/Pacific Islanders, and 1.0 percent American Indian/Alaskan Native citizens (U.S. Census Bureau, 2004). There is evidence that children from minority backgrounds are at increased risk for trauma exposure and posttraumatic stress disorder during disasters (Norris et al., 2002a,b).

Special Categories of Children with Special Needs

Consideration must be given to other subsets of children who are at increased risk for exposure to disaster stressors. These include youth who are confined to juvenile detention centers, substance abuse treatment centers and halfway houses; children who are placed in shelters for domestic violence; and children in youth hostels and centers for homeless and runaway youth, as well as those who remain on the streets. As described above, many children chronically experience the stressors associated with poverty and economic disadvantage, ethnic and racial discrimination, and illegal immigration. Many of these youth are outside of the reach of systems that provide safety, shelter, services and support during disasters.

Interventions

Pre-impact Phase:

Children with special needs require medical and community interventions that are mobilized to ensure the safety and protection of the child. This includes child protective services, medical care venues, foster care placement, and residential care when indicated. Children with identified special needs are usually in an ongoing intervention program prior to the occurrence of a disaster in their community. Since programs for special needs children are multifaceted and time-phased, continuity of care is essential for optimal outcomes. This requires a sustained investment of resources and planning for continuity of operations during extreme events. Pre-disaster planning must prioritize support for the entire family with special needs children since optimal therapeutic outcome is closely tied to parental and family influences.

In the pre-impact phase, efforts should be made by both municipal and mental health professionals to promote community contingency plans for children who have been exposed to cumulative traumatic experiences and who will need to have special consideration at the time of disaster. Parents need to prepare for the eventuality of emergency situations such as disasters that may interfere with the continuity of healthcare, family stability and social supports. It is important for families to be informed about the potential hazards that are likely to occur in the local area. It is prudent to anticipate and prepare for such emergencies by becoming informed about community disaster and evacuation plans, school plans for reuniting children and families at the time of disaster, and the locations of special needs shelters. Parents are encouraged to develop alliances with healthcare providers, to prepare emergency supply kits with the child's critical medical supplies and necessary medications, and to have contingency plans to request and receive assistance from other family members in time of need.

Impact Phase:

During disaster impact, children in harm's way are exposed to a range of disaster stressors. This is the time to put into operation the family's emergency plans for ensuring continuing health care and family stability. Knowing that previous exposure to psychosocial adversities increases the vulnerability to additional traumatic exposure, special needs children should be prioritized for evacuation to safe environments with ongoing provision of services in order to minimize the intensity of exposure and the disruption of care.

Post-Impact Phase:

Post-impact, the focus for special needs children should be on maintaining or rapidly restoring supportive services and care environments. Accurate assessment of the child's symptoms facilitates tailored and customized intervention as needed in the aftermath of the disaster experience. Every effort should be made to enhance the child's coping capacities and resiliency, and to mitigate the child's uncertainty, physical discomfort and perception of social isolation or separation from loved ones.

Particular attention should be given to providing disaster recovery and behavioral health support for the parents and caregivers of special needs children. The parent's management of essential care is critical for mitigating the traumatic events for the child.

Assessment and intervention at the time of disaster impact and its aftermath must be sensitized to culturally-competent practices. A traumatic event is interpreted and given meaning within the context of ethnic and cultural values and beliefs. During disasters, care and support must be provided to disaster-affected populations that reflect a mix of cultures, value systems, health beliefs and primary languages.

It is necessary to assess the level of acculturation and corresponding level of "acculturative stress." For example, a child may feel comfortable speaking English and be more acculturated than the parents who may prefer to speak their native language. When possible, use an interpreter or find a provider who is fluent in the family's native language. A culturally-competent assessment will address issues of cultural identity, values and health beliefs, treatment expectations, family supports, cross-generational differences in acculturation and trauma associated with migration and relocation. It is important to perceive the child as part of the family unit and to engage the family as a whole. For example, the cultural value of "familismo" in the Hispanic community requires that helpers recognize the importance of engaging the entire family in any assessment or integration process.

Summary

Children with special needs include the psychiatrically and medically ill, those who have suffered from multiple episodes of child maltreatment from parents and caretakers, the developmentally disabled, children in foster care and children who are disadvantaged by poverty. During disasters and extreme events, the child with special needs may have reduced resiliency and fewer resources to manage the repeated exposures to stressors, leading to heightened risk for psychological disorders, including disaster-associated posttraumatic stress symptoms. Special needs children must receive priority consideration in disaster planning to maintain continuity of care and to minimize traumatic exposure.

Center for Disaster & Extreme Event Preparedness

CH 6

Traumatic Bereavement

Chapter 6

Traumatic Bereavement

On successful completion of this chapter you should be able to:

1) Recognize the concepts of loss and bereavement
2) Recognize the special features of bereavement in childhood
3) Identify the stages of bereavement
4) Recognize key treatment issues for childhood bereavement

Key Concepts

- Children exposed to disaster may experience the death of a parent or other significant person.
- Children's psychological reactions to the death of a loved one are influenced by the child's age, level of psychological and emotional maturity, extent of adaptive and coping capacities, and understanding of death.
- Children's responses are shaped by the child's relationship to the deceased, the circumstances of death, previous experience with death, and available social support systems.
- Children's psychological reactions to the death of a loved one are variable and diverse; however, the majority of bereaved children do not develop psychiatric disorders.

Source: FEMA photolibrary

Introduction

When mass casualties occur in a disaster, survivors may be exposed to scenes of death. Death from disaster usually occurs suddenly, unexpectedly, and with little predictability, striking down the healthy and taking life prematurely. Bereavement has been defined as the fact of loss through death. Bereavement reactions include both psychological and physiological responses to bereavement. Grief refers to the emotions associated with bereavement, and mourning is the social expression of grief.

Four percent of children in the United States experience the death of a parent before the age of 15 (National Center for Health Statistics, 1997). The early death of a parent most frequently occurs as the result of trauma. Children are twice as likely to lose their father as to lose their mother. The loss of other family members such as siblings, grandparents and other loved ones, while less traumatic, nevertheless, may have an enduring psychological effect on the developing child.

Children's early exposure to death, the discovery that life is not permanent, the realization that the body is susceptible to harm, and the loss of important, care-giving relationships in their daily lives, are traumatic experiences. The death of a parent or family member is usually sudden and often brutal. Children suffer not only from the premature loss of a family member, but also from exposure to the cruel and violent nature of the death. Psychological and physiological reactions to bereavement are processed differently in children compared with adults because of the child's cognitive, emotional, and physical immaturity.

Key Definitions

Bereavement: The fact of loss through death
Grief: Emotions associated with bereavement
Bereavement Reactions: Psychological or physiological responses to bereavement
Mourning: The social expression of grief
Anticipatory Grief: Emotions experienced in anticipation of an impending death

Source: Osterweis et al., 1984

Childhood Bereavement

The death of a significant person in a child's life is among the most stressful events that a young person can experience. A child who has lost a parent, sibling or loved one must find a way to cope with the immediate impact of the death on his or her life. Simultaneously, the child must begin the process of mourning and resume normal everyday activities. Adults in the child's life, in the midst of their own grief, are frequently confused and uncertain about how to respond supportively to a child. The task of the surviving parent or other caretakers is to facilitate the child's process of coping, mourning, and resuming normal life activities.

Basic Facts

• 4 percent of children experience the death of a parent before 15 years of age

• Approximately 1,300 children lost a parent on September 11, 2001

• 40,000 children die each year

• 7,000-12,000 children experience parental suicide each year

• 1.2 million adults have experienced early parent death

• 8 million people experience the death of an immediate family member each year

• 800,000 persons become a widow or /widower each year

• Approximately 30,000 suicides occur annually in the United States

Source: National Center for Health Statistics (1997); Weller et al., (2002)

Children's psychological reactions to the death of a loved one are influenced by the child's age, level of psychological and emotional maturity, extent of adaptive and coping capacities, and understanding of death. Children's responses are shaped by the child's relationship to the deceased, the circumstances of death, the child's previous experience with death, and available social support systems (Dowdney, 2000). Children who experience the death of a parent are usually concerned with several questions: Did I cause this death to happen? Is it going to happen to me? Who is going to take care of me? Children don't understand chance happenings and look for sources of blame. They also begin to fear that if death happened to someone close to them, death might happen to them. Children experience an increasing sense of vulnerability coupled with concerns about abandonment, wondering who is going to take care of them and provide support.

While children do not usually experience intense or prolonged emotional and behavioral grief reactions, their mourning processes usually last longer than those of adults. Since bereavement is a process that continues over time, children often experience thoughts and emotions related to parental loss during life milestones and transitions such as separation experiences, going away to camp or school, receiving recognition for achievements, graduation, getting married, or giving birth to their own children.

Parental Bereavement

Particularly poignant is the parent's loss of a child. Both the Oklahoma City Bombing and the September 11 World Trade Center bombing resulted in the tragic deaths of children. The discovery that one's child is untimely ripped away from one's family leaves the parent with a pervasive feeling of despair and emptiness. The grief of parents following the loss of a child "is more intense and prolonged than other losses" (Raphael, 2006). Parents are at increased risk for suicidal behavior in the month following such a loss and for enduring symptoms of depression and anxiety extending for 5-10 years. When the child dies as a result of trauma, parental grief may be confounded with posttraumatic stress reactions (Breslau et al., 1998).

Stages of Bereavement

The psychological responses to bereavement may be described in three stages: 1) acute/immediate effects, 2) intermediate responses, and 3) long-term effects.

Acute/Immediate Effects

The immediate and acute symptoms following the death of a loved one are usually shock, disbelief, tearfulness and a sense of unreality; combined with a spectrum of emotions such as sadness, fear, anger, helplessness and anxiety. Often, there is loss of appetite, sleep disturbances and aching pain in the pit of the stomach. Bereavement is accompanied by disturbances in thinking with decreased concentration, diminished capacity for problem solving and inability to think about consequences or plan for the future. Younger children may manifest regression, agitation, disorganized behaviors, clinging dependency, bodily symptoms, loss of bladder or bowel control and nightmares.

Kranzler, et al. (1990) studied preschool children, ages 3-6 years, who had lost a parent. Compared with non-bereaved children, children who had lost a parent were more scared and unhappy, and experienced significantly more emotional and behavioral symptoms. In contrast to adults, children's grief responses were more episodic and situational but less pervasive. Others have noted that children often manifest less sadness and emotional turmoil than adults in the immediate aftermath of the loss of a loved one.

Intermediate Effects

In the aftermath of bereavement, children may experience ongoing difficulties in social relatedness including social withdrawal, somatic symptoms, waves of distress, a preoccupation with the image of the departed, yearning for the deceased, impaired vocational and school adjustment, nightmares, loss of appetite, weight loss, sleep disturbances, suicidal thoughts, loss of interest in normally enjoyed activities, a limited range of emotions or excessive emotionality and clinging-dependent regressive behaviors. Children, depending on their level of cognitive development, may want explanations as to the cause of what happened and may search for blame. Not understanding cause-and-effect, young children may blame themselves for the death. Children may neglect self-care, fail to perform household chores or experience a decline in academic or work performance. Angry, aggressive and antisocial behaviors may occur in addition to a spectrum of anxiety and depressive symptoms.

In a study of children, ages 5-12 years, conducted three months after the death of a parent, the following rates of bereavement symptoms were observed: loss of appetite (24 percent), depressed mood (61 percent), loss of interest (45 percent), feelings of guilt/worthlessness (37 percent) and sleep disturbances (32 percent) (Weller et al., 1991).

Long-Term Reactions

In the continuing aftermath, children may experience further decrements in academic performance; a range of anxiety, depression and behavioral symptoms; bodily symptoms; interpersonal and social adjustment problems; and decreased self-efficacy. Worden and Silverman (1996) studied 125 children who had experienced the death of a parent compared to matched controls. Bereaved children were more likely to exhibit lower self-esteem and lower scores on locus of control. Approximately one-fifth of the bereaved children manifested serious emotional and behavioral disturbances requiring intervention. Two years after the parental death, preadolescent girls were more prone to experience anxiety, depression and aggressive behaviors while adolescent boys were more socially withdrawn and exhibited more social problems.

Adults identified as experiencing maternal death before age 10 were observed to have increased risks for panic attacks and simple phobias (Tweed et al., 1989). Breier (1988) has suggested that the child who experiences the early death of a parent is at increased risk for psychiatric disorders in adult life (particularly depression), although the risk is diminished for the bereaved child who maintains a good relationship with the surviving parent and experiences satisfying peer relationships.

Developmental Effects

Children's understanding of death is greatly influenced by cognitive development (Spence & Brent, 1984). Generally, younger children may confuse death with going to sleep or they may think of death as a journey and expect the lost loved one to return. Children, ages 4 to 6, may know that death occurs, but they may often think of it as temporary and reversible.

The preschool child is unable to understand death and will manifest distress in behaviors and bodily complaints. The child may exhibit clinging and dependent behaviors, loss of previous developmental achievements such as bowel and bladder control, inattention, disorganized behaviors, tantrums, bodily symptoms, sleep and appetite disturbances and a variety of anxiety and mood symptoms.

The school-age child often imagines death as a ghost or man on a black horse and fears being "hurt". Death is seen as frightening and as something that happens to older persons. By ages 8 or 9, children have some understanding of the finality, inevitability and irreversibility of death. The child may manifest anxiety, abandonment fears, depressed mood, academic and learning problems, social withdrawal, sleep and appetite disturbances and a range of behavioral problems. Boys are more likely than girls to express their grief through hyperactivity and aggression and appear to be more vulnerable to the psychological effects of early parent death (Dowdney, 2000).

The adolescent may experience a sense of social estrangement, fears of early death, anxiety and mood symptoms, somatic ills, anger, guilt and behavioral problems and may take flight into the pursuit of pleasurable experiences or become more socially withdrawn and narrow the scope of life.

Even children with seemingly age-appropriate bereavement reactions may experience a relapse or exacerbation when confronted with subsequent stressors, symbolic reminders or additional losses. The bereavement process is a long-lasting and continuing emotional struggle to achieve emotional resolution.

Table 6.1
Grief and Developmental Stages

Age	Understanding of Death	Expressions of Grief
Infancy to 2 years	• Not yet able to understand death • Separation from mother causes changes	• Quietness, crankiness, decreased activity, poor sleep, weight loss
2-6 years	• Death is like sleeping	• Many questions (How does she go to the bathroom? How does she eat?) • Problems in eating, sleeping and bladder and bowel control • Fear of abandonment • Tantrums
	• Dead person continues to live and function in some ways • Death is temporary, not final • Dead person can come back to life	• Magical thinking (Did I think something or do something that caused the death? Like when I said I hate you and I wish you would die?)
6-9 years	• Death is perceived as a person or spirit (skeleton, ghost, bogeyman)	• Curiosity about death • Specific questions • Exaggerated fears about school
	• Death is final and frightening	• Aggressive behaviors (especially boys) • Concerns about imaginary illnesses
	• Death happens to others, it won't happen to ME	• Feelings of abandonment
9 and older	• Everyone will die	• Heightened emotions, guilt, anger, shame • Increased anxiety over own death • Mood swings
	• Death is final and cannot be changed	• Fear of rejection; not wanting to be different from peers
	• Even I will die	• Changes in eating habits • Sleep problems • Regressive behaviors (loss of interest in outside activities) • Impulsive behaviors • Guilt about being alive (especially related to death of a brother, sister or peer)

Childhood Bereavement and Psychological Morbidity

Studies of bereaved children who have experienced the sudden death of a parent have indicated that they experience more anxiety, depression and disruptive behaviors than their non-bereaved counterparts (Van Eederweigh et al., 1985; Kranzler et al., 1990; Weller et al., 1991; Worden & Silverman, 1996). Gleser and colleagues (1981) noted that in the Buffalo Creek disaster, bereavement and threat to life were the predominant stressors giving rise to prolonged psychopathology. In a study of children, ages 5-12 years, conducted three months after the death of a parent, Weller, et al. (1991) found that 37 percent met diagnostic criteria for major depressive disorder and 61 percent experienced suicidal thoughts. The suicidal ideation represented a longing to be with the deceased parent (reunion fantasy) rather than the devaluation of the child's own life, and none of the children attempted suicide. Surviving parents were not fully aware of their children's depressive symptoms, a finding that underscores the importance of interviewing bereaved children and not relying solely on parents' reports of their children's symptoms.

Childhood Bereavement Reactions

61%	Dysphoria (Distressing emotions)
61%	Suicidal ideation
45%	Loss of interest
37%	Agitation/retardation
37%	Guilt/worthlessness
37%	Major Depressive Disorder
32%	Sleep disturbances
24%	Loss of appetite
11%	Fatigue

Source: Weller et al., 1991

A study of Israeli children, ages 2-10 years, conducted for several years following the death of their fathers in war, found that more than half demonstrated fears, over-dependent behavior, and temper tantrums (Elizur & Kaffman 1982, 1983). Forty percent had emotional and behavioral problems of such severity as to interfere with adjustment at home, in school and with peers. The severity of the bereavement reactions was influenced by the quality of the relationship with the father prior to his death, the ability of the mother to share her grief with the child and the availability of extended family members to offer support. Other studies confirm that the psychological impact of parental death is predominantly mediated by the availability of extended family support systems, the relationship to the remaining parent and other social and economic adversities (Breier et al., 1988; Harrington & Harrison, 1999). Protective factors that help buffer the impact of bereavement are high self-esteem, scholastic competence and ability to use available social support networks (Harrington & Harrison, 1999).

Risk Factors Associated with Sustained Bereavement

- Personal importance of the relationship
- Quality of relationship to the deceased
- Sudden and unexpected death
- Circumstances of the death
- Cognitive maturity of the child
- Not having the chance to say goodbye
- Quality of family and social supports
- Child's specific coping and adaptive skills
- Socio-economic supports

Death of a Sibling

Loss of a sibling can cause immediate and long-lasting emotional and behavioral effects on children. The death of a sibling is the loss of a peer relationship complicated by the special and ambivalent bond between siblings. Siblings share a unique relationship in having the same parents and having shared confidences separate from those shared with their parents. The surviving child may experience feelings of guilt associated with sibling rivalry or may harbor feelings of blame that the parents failed to protect their sibling from death. When the loss of a sibling leaves the surviving sibling as an only child, the bereavement experience is particularly difficult.

Worden & Silverman (1996) suggest several differences between parental and sibling death. The loss of a child in a family carries emotional and behavioral effects on the parenting of the remaining children. Parents may become overprotective of the remaining children. Parents may also burden the surviving children with a "replacement child script" in which expectations envisioned for the now-deceased child are imposed on the remaining siblings.

Attending the Funeral

Therapists are often asked whether or not children should attend funerals. While the literature is contradictory and anecdotal on this point, therapists generally concur that if children are under 5 or 6 years of age, they cannot process the meaning nor understand the significance of what transpires. Increasing evidence does suggest, however, that when children want to go to a funeral, it may be psychologically beneficial if they are adequately prepared, informed, and accompanied by an adult who can be emotionally and cognitively available to comfort them and to manage any distress or grief occurring during the service. Participation in the funeral service may help children to remember loved ones and may provide an opportunity to say goodbye.

Treatment

Usually, adults have the task of informing a child of the death of a family member, providing some explanation commensurate with the child's level of understanding and ascribing meaning to the death in line with the family's religious beliefs. Death should not be likened to sleep or a long journey, but rather explained in terms of cessation of bodily activities. A number of children's books (*Charlotte's Web*, by E. B. White) are useful for helping children to understand death as a natural phenomenon. Such readings increase awareness that exposure to death is part of the life experience.

Since grief is a normal reaction to bereavement, treatment may not be necessary. It may be difficult to distinguish between a normal grief reaction and one that develops

into symptoms of depression and anxiety that interfere with the child's normal development and ability to meet the demands of everyday life. Depressive symptoms and suicidal thoughts are not uncommon. Caretakers and professionals should be aware of the potential for significant behavioral problems, emotional distress, bodily symptoms, declines in school performance or impairment in interpersonal and social relationships for grieving children. Since bereavement is the normal psychological response to the death of a loved one, providers must be judicious in prescribing treatment interventions.

Indicators for treatment following bereavement may include a history of previous emotional or behavioral problems or current depressive, anxiety and behavioral symptoms that interfere with the child's progressive development. Usually a child is not identified as having significant emotional or behavioral problems until 6 to 12 months after the loss. Treatment goals should focus on providing a safe place, facilitating the acceptance of death, supporting new attachments and adjustments, restoring normal development, resolving mixed feelings, examining both positive and negative memories, clarifying cognitive distortions and identifying mood states and traumatic reminders. Providers must distinguish the psychological effects associated with posttraumatic stress responses from those associated with bereavement.

Therapeutic interventions for bereaved children range from acute crisis intervention and brief psychosocial intervention to more intensive cognitive-behavioral therapy, psychodynamic therapy, play therapy, and family/group therapy approaches.

Crisis intervention focuses on supporting positive adaptive and coping strategies, providing psychoeducation about expectable reactions that may be experienced, providing outlet for expression of feelings, reframing distorted thinking, and applying anxiety reduction techniques. The therapist stresses that the psychological response is a normally-expected reaction to loss. The bereaved child is encouraged to restore routines, engage in health-promoting activities and participate in social relationships as well as normal school and work activities.

Table 6.2
Children's Thoughts, Emotions and Physiological Reactions

	Understanding of Death	Expressions of Grief
Thoughts	• Focus on death and images of horror	• Focus on lost person and images of person
Emotions	• Longing for security/safety • Anxiety about threat • Anger, irritability and reminders of threat • Numbing	• Yearning for lost person • Separation anxiety • Anger • Sadness
Physiological Reactions	• "Fight-or-flight" reaction • Focus on potential further threat • Exaggerated startle reactions	• Attentive scanning for lost person • Response to cues of that person

Trauma-focused cognitive behavioral therapy (TF-CBT) is well established as an effective treatment for posttraumatic stress disorder, anxiety and depressive symptoms and child sexual abuse (Pine & Cohen, 2002). TF-CBT encompasses many techniques such as cognitive restructuring, exposure techniques and emotional/information processing strategies.

Young children often experience feelings of blame and guilt for the death of a loved one, or other inappropriate attributions for traumatic events. Cognitive restructuring explores the child's thoughts about a traumatic event with the goal of correcting inaccurate thinking or "cognitive distortions" (Pine & Cohen, 2002). Through TF-CBT, children learn to examine their thoughts more critically, not to over-generalize and to selectively attend to thoughts that are more accurate and helpful.

Cohen and colleagues (2006) conducted an uncontrolled pilot intervention study of 22 children (ages 6-17 years) with significant child traumatic grief and posttraumatic stress symptoms, along with their primary caretakers. Children were referred to an urban outpatient child trauma program after losing a loved one in a variety of traumatic events including accidents, medical causes, suicide, homicide, and drug overdose. The trauma-focused components included

sessions on improving affect modulation, stress reduction, trauma-specific exposure, preserving positive memories and defining the meaning of the loss. More recently, Cohen et al. (2006) employed a modified 12-session version of their intervention with a sample of 39 children, ages 6 to 17 years, referred to outpatient treatment for child trauma and traumatic grief. Children showed significant improvement in grief, traumatic grief, mood, anxiety, posttraumatic stress and behavior, but not in depression.

One CBT intervention facilitates mourning by both the bereaved child and the surviving parent during a series of 3-5 family-based sessions (Black & Urbanowicz, 1987). Salloum et al. (2001) were able to achieve significant reductions in anxiety, re-experiencing and avoidance symptoms by applying a CBT group intervention for adolescents, ages 11-19 years, who had lost a family member to homicide.

Exposure techniques are often a part of CBT and include reliving memories, writing personal narratives of the trauma and maintaining a journal. The guided exposure provides a means by which the child can gradually absorb a traumatic experience over time. These strategies provide opportunities to confront traumatic reminders in order to reduce the child's negative emotions; cognitive distortions; damaged self-efficacy; and feelings of guilt, anger and helplessness. Therapeutic activities may incorporate relaxation training and use of psycho-educational materials. Many TF-CBT models include a parent component that parallels the child's intervention, with the goal of enhancing parent-child communication as a part of the child's treatment (Pine & Cohen, 2002).

Play therapy relies on children's natural propensity to express their innermost conflicts in the symbolic world of play. Children attempt to solve problems through play. Play involves wish fulfillment and facilitates expression of pent-up feelings. In play therapy, children replace passivity with action and achieve mastery through experimentation and trial action. The child moves at his or her own pace with the therapist's clarifications and interventions. The therapist helps the child to understand and give meaning to grief and assists the child in restoring normal age-appropriate developmental progression and adaptive coping strategies.

Recommendations for Parents

- **MEET AS A FAMILY:** Provide a sense of a family working together to plan for the changes in family circumstances. The best support against loss is the love and support of other family members. Be sure to include the child as much as possible in family decisions.

- **REASSURE THE CHILD:** Be a calm presence as much as possible. Let the child know the family is planning on how to stay together.

- **RECOGNIZE THAT CHILDREN ARE CHILDREN:** Children at different ages have different ideas about death. Help them to understand the meaning of death in its finality but resonant with religious beliefs.

- **TALK TO YOUR CHILD IN LANGUAGE THAT HE OR SHE CAN UNDERSTAND:** Explain to your child what happened, what is happening and what is going to happen in a language that he or she can understand.

- **LISTEN TO YOUR CHILD'S FEELINGS:** Younger children may not be able to express their grief, fears and anxieties. It is often helpful to label the feelings and to validate them in a sensitive, supportive and shared manner. Where possible, join with your child in understanding their feelings in a way that conveys that you will manage the situation. Allow your children to mourn or grieve.

- **LISTEN TO YOUR CHILD'S THOUGHTS:** Try to understand your child's perceptions and thoughts about what has happened. Be aware of a readiness for self-blame, anger and guilt. Listen and answer their questions honestly.

- **ENCOURAGE CHILDREN TO TALK:** Provide an atmosphere of acceptance in which the child feels free to express anxieties, grief, fears and worries.

- **ROUTINIZE AND NORMALIZE YOUR CHILD'S LIFE:** Get back to a routine as quickly as possible. This indicates to your children that you feel secure and are beginning to manage the situation.

Summary

Children exposed to disaster may experience the death of a parent or other significant person. Bereavement reactions, grief and mourning are mediated by such factors as age, gender, psychological and emotional maturity, personality, adaptive and coping strategies, relationship to the deceased, circumstances of death, degree of participation in the dying process, previous experiences with death and availability of a social support system. Psychological reactions are variable and diverse; however, the majority of bereaved children do not develop psychiatric disorders. High self-esteem, calm temperament, scholastic competence, and the capacity to derive support from relationships with surviving family members serve as protective factors.

Chapter 7

Child and Family Assessment

On successful completion of this chapter you should be able to:

1) Identify the critical elements elicited in the assessment process for disaster-exposed children
2) Describe the use of child and parent/caregiver psychological interviews to provide multiple sources of information for assessing the trauma-exposed child
3) Identify the leading assessment instruments and rating scales

Key Concepts

- The assessment of the child and family is critical to determine the full extent of the child's psychological responses to life-threatening events.
- The assessment process must be sensitive to the child's level of cognitive and emotional development.
- Optimal assessment uses multiple sources of information to provide understanding of the psychological responses and post-disaster psychosocial functioning of the family.
- Assessment procedures may be used as part of a triage process to identify children at high risk and for in-depth analysis of the psychological functioning of a disaster-exposed child.

Introduction

Disasters and traumatic events confront children and adults with a variety of stressors during the impact phase and in the aftermath. The awareness that children encounter the same constellation of stressors as adults has increased the focus on evaluation of children exposed to traumatic events. Careful assessment of children's psychological reactions is essential for identifying children at elevated risk for disaster-related psychosocial consequences and those in need of therapeutic intervention as well as accurately diagnosing trauma-related symptoms.

Screening

Screening and evaluation of children and their families are conducted in a phase-specific manner over time. Informal assessment occurs on an ongoing basis as first-line responders, school personnel, and public health professionals interact with children and families who have been exposed to disaster. First responders begin the process of identifying children at high risk. As schools reopen, systematic screening procedures may be implemented in the school setting to help identify at-risk children and to intervene as necessary on behalf of these children and their families. This process is guided by school counselors and crisis intervention specialists (Cohen et al., 2006).

In some instances, it will be necessary to refer children and their families to a mental health professional for formal assessment. Referrals are warranted for symptoms and behaviors that are severe and hinder the child's ability to meet the demands of everyday life. For the younger child, indicators include excessive and persistent fearfulness, clinging and dependent behaviors, temper tantrums, agitation, hyperactivity, loss of bladder and bowel control and disturbing nightmares. For the older child or adolescent, symptoms of concern include hyperarousal, anxiety, panic, depressed mood and such maladaptive behaviors as belligerence, family and interpersonal conflicts and misuse of substances.

Clinical Assessment

The evaluation process is complex and multifaceted. It requires not only an interview with the child but also information from other informants such as parents, family members, teachers and other significant persons in the child's life. Since the family system may either hinder or facilitate the child's psychological adaptation and coping strategies, it is essential to evaluate the effects of the traumatic stressor on the various members of the family with particular focus on the parental response. Clinicians generally agree that family and parental support mitigates the risk for posttraumatic stress symptoms (Cohen et al., 1998).

Before engaging children and parents in a psychological interview, safeguards should be in place to ensure that the child and family members are safe and secure, that life sustaining provisions are assured and that measures have been taken to provide continuity of support systems.

The parent interview elicits objective information regarding the nature and severity of the trauma exposure, stressors encountered, psychological responses (including possible posttraumatic stress symptoms), behavior problems, mood and anxiety symptoms, multiple unexplained physical symptoms (MUPS) and concurrent psychological disorders (Table 7.1). The parent interview explores the child's developmental history; risk and protective factors; parent and family responses to the disaster; and the ethnic, religious and cultural context of the traumatic event.

Table 7.1
Critical Elements Elicited in the Assessment Process

History of the Traumatic Exposure

- Assess the traumatic event as an extreme stressor
  - What is the nature of the traumatic event?
- Does it qualify as an imagined or actual threat to bodily integrity or to life itself?
- What was the level of exposure?
  - Direct physical impact, visual or media exposure, interpersonal relatedness to victims
  - What was the intensity and duration of exposure?

Family History

- Were the parents and other family members exposed?
- What was the parental or family response to the traumatic event?
  - Parents' emotional and behavioral symptoms
  - Parents' psychopathology
  - Parents' reaction to the child's distress
  - Family mental health history
  - Stability and functionality of the family support system

Inventory of Stressors

- Bereavement
- Separation from loved ones
- Loss of home/shelter
- Loss of school or other routine activities
- Relationship to peer group
- Physical injury

Child's Developmental History

- Previous exposure to traumatic events
- Coping behaviors
- Psychosocial adjustment
- Psychological morbidity
- History of psychological treatments
- Medical history
- School and academic performance

Child Interview

- Obtain the child's report of what happened
- Explore the child's attributions (their understanding of why it happened, their role in it happening, their thoughts and feelings about how they have responded, and their understanding of how the traumatic event has affected their emotional and behavior well-being)
- Complete a symptom inventory
- Assess for acute stress disorder (ASD) and post-traumatic stress disorder (PTSD)
- Assess for psychiatric comorbidity
  - Mood disorder
  - Anxiety disorder
  - Adjustment disorders
  - Disruptive behaviors: attention deficit/ hyperactivity disorder (ADHD), conduct disorder(CD), oppositional defiant disorder (ODD)
  - Symptoms of hyperarousal
  - Substance abuse
  - Dissociative disorders
  - Physical symptoms
- Assess self-efficacy, coping and adaptive capacities
- Assess the child's capacities to seek and use help from adults

In a separate interview, children are provided an opportunity to describe their perceptions and understanding of what happened and their reactions to the traumatic experience. It is important to establish a sense of ease with the child, to slowly win the child's confidence through friendly interactions and to find the child's level of discourse. In most instances, children are able to tell their stories in words or use nonverbal means for relating what happened as expressed in play, story-telling, and drawings. School-age children are usually able to provide self-reports of their traumatic exposures. Direct questioning is often necessary to fill in the gaps but the questions should be sensitive to the child's comfort, emotional availability and cognitive development.

The Child Interview: Direct Questions to Consider

- Have you been hurt or injured?
- Have you seen anyone get hurt badly?
- Has anyone in your family been hurt?
- Have you seen anything really scary and frightening?
- Do you ever have any scary dreams or nightmares?
- How do you sleep at night?
- What was the most upsetting and scary part of the experience?
- Do you ever see or hear anything that reminds you of something really scary?
- Who makes you feel safe?

Source: Modified from Bostic & King (2007)

Child assessment requires collecting information regarding the child's perceptions and understanding, his or her theory of causality, self-attributions, resiliency and the child's repertoire of adaptive and coping mechanisms for regulating emotions and impulse control.

While gathering information through the parent and child interviews, the clinician should be aware of how the child's level of cognitive and emotional development influences the expression of posttraumatic stress symptoms. Because of their cognitive and emotional immaturity, children are often unable to fully discuss their distress and impairment. Infants and toddlers are limited in their expressive language skills and capabilities for describing their subjective experiences. Preschool children are unable to verbalize symptoms of distress, describe intrusive thoughts or flashbacks or identify sources of physical complaints. For preschool children, internal emotional states are revealed through behaviors such as clinging dependency, temper tantrums, separation anxiety, fear of the dark and sleep and appetite disturbances (Scheeringa et al., 1995).

Piaget (1967) observed that younger children do not recognize the existence of chance happenings. The younger child assumes that everything that happens is related to something that he or she did or did not do. Before the age of seven years, children often attribute purpose or intention to events that others realize are chance happenings.

For school-age children, the focus shifts to assessment of behavioral expressions of inner turmoil. Psychological distress may manifest through play and behavioral symptoms rather than through verbal description. Hyperactivity, sleep and appetite disturbances, decrements in school performance, inability to concentrate, physical symptoms, irritability and sibling rivalry are common responses to the traumatic situation. In contrast, older children are often able to express unpleasant internal emotional states in words, discuss the subjective experience of the trauma exposure and ascribe meaning to the event.

PTSD Rating Scales/Instruments

In the field of disaster psychiatry, assessment has been strengthened by the development of instruments to define disaster-specific stressors and reactions (Saylor & Deroma, 2002). Standardized assessment instruments target specific dimensions of disaster or trauma exposure and identify stressors, emotional and behavioral reactions and attributions of causation. Optimal assessment requires adherence to the basic principles of scientific research and practice, including the use of multiple information sources

and the selection of well-established, reliable and valid assessment measures (Finch & Daugherty, 1993).

In order to properly define the assessment approach, the clinician must clarify the goals and define the key questions for investigation. One primary distinction is to determine whether the assessment will be used for triage purposes or as a tool to evaluate the child's psychological responses to the traumatic event. For example, is the goal of assessment to identify children with clinical psychological disorders such as PTSD or depression, or to identify children with problematic behaviors (that do not qualify as disorders)?

Balaban (2006) identified five field-tested screening instruments designed for children and adolescents that are applicable for use in disaster and emergency settings. Each of the five employs a standardized, scientifically-validated questionnaire that can be administered by clinicians or non-clinicians in 60 minutes or less (Table 7.2). Among the five measures, Balaban concluded that the PTSD Reaction Index (UCLA PTSD-RI) is the most appropriate measure for evaluating children across a wide variety of disasters. This measure, now available in multiple languages, is inexpensive, simple, rapidly administered and scored and supported by sound scientific research (Balaban, 2006).

Table 7.2
Instruments for Assessing Post-Traumatic Symptoms and PTSD

Instrument	Purpose	Availability	Ages	Length/administration time
UCLA PTSD Reaction Index for DSM IV	To assess post-trauma symptoms and PTSD in children	No cost; rpynoos@mednet.ucla.edu	6–17	22 items 20–30 minutes
Impact of Events Scale- Revised (IES-R)	To measure symptoms of PTSD after a traumatic event	No cost; available on many websites, such as http://www.swin.edu.au/victims/resources/assessment/ptsd/ies-r.html A 13-item version of the IES-R (IES-13) developed for children affected by war is available at http://www.childrenandwar.org/CRIES-13.doc	Used with children as young as 7 (not designed for children)	22 items 10–15 minutes
Child PTSD Symptom Scale (CPSS)	To evaluate symptoms and functional impairment related to PTSD	No cost; foa@mail.med.upenn.edu	8–18	24 items 15 minutes
Posttraumatic Stress Symptoms in Children (PTSS-C)	To identify pediatric post-traumatic symptoms in chaotic disaster contexts	No cost; Abdulbaghi.Ahmad@bupinst.uu.se	6–18	30 items 30 minutes
Trauma Symptom Checklist for Children (TSCC)	To assess PTSD symptoms after trauma, particularly sexual abuse	Licensed through http://www.parinc.com	7–16	54 items 20 minutes

Source: Balaban, 2006

Instruments for Depression, Anxiety and Behavioral Problems

In addition to posttraumatic stress symptoms, mood and anxiety symptoms are also common responses to the life-threatening situations and multiple losses that characterize disasters. Standardized instruments for the broader range of psychological reactions are presented in Table 7.3.

Table 7.3
Instruments for Assessing Depression, Anxiety and Behavior

Instrument	Purpose	Availability	Ages	Length/administration time
INSTRUMENTS FOR ASSESSING DEPRESSION				
Children's Depression Inventory (CDI)	To measure depressive symptom severity in children	Licensed through http://www.mhs.com	7–17	27 items 5–10 minutes
Depression Self-Rating Scale (DSRS)	To measure symptoms of depression	No cost; contact author	6–13	18 items
INSTRUMENTS FOR ASSESSING ANXIETY				
Multidimensional Anxiety Scale for Children (MASC)	To assess anxiety symptoms in children	Licensed through http://www.mhs.com	8–19	39 items 15 minutes (10-item short form also available)
Revised Children's Manifest Anxiety Scale (RCMAS)	To evaluate anxiety symptoms in children	No cost; available on many websites, including http://www.swin.edu.au/victims/resources/assessment/affect/rcmas.html	6–19	37 items
INSTRUMENTS FOR ASSESSING BEHAVIOR				
Pediatric Emotional Distress Scale (PEDS)	To measure post-traumatic behavioral problems in children	No cost; Conway.saylor@citadel.edu	2–10	21 items 10–15 minutes
Revised Behavior Problem Checklist (RBPC)	To rate problem behavior in adolescents and young children	Licensed through http://www.parinc.com	5–18	89 items 20 minutes

Source: Balaban, 2006

Summary

The assessment of the child and family is critical to determine the full extent of the child's psychological responses to life-threatening events. Optimal assessment uses multiple sources of information to provide understanding of the psychological responses and post-disaster psychosocial functioning of the family. Assessment procedures may be used as part of a triage process to identify children at high risk or for in-depth analysis of the psychological functioning of a disaster-exposed child.

A careful assessment and clinical history is taken from the parents or caretakers. The child interview should focus on engagement strategies, friendly interaction, empathic listening and sensitivity to the child's emotional state and cognitive level. The use of nonverbal modalities such as play, story-telling or drawings as well as some direct questioning is necessary to elicit the child's perception, understanding and response to the traumatic situation. Standardized instruments for the assessment of posttraumatic stress symptoms and the broader range of psychological reactions are often useful.

CH 8

Interventions

Chapter 8

Interventions

On successful completion of this chapter you should be able to:

1) Identify the guiding principles for intervention with children and adolescents exposed to disasters
2) Describe the guiding principles of early psychosocial intervention in the immediate aftermath of disaster
3) Describe the key principles and core actions of Psychological First Aid
4) Recognize the range of available interventions following large-scale disaster

Key Concepts

- Evidence-based science has begun to identify the most promising interventions for use with disaster survivors.
- Interventions are provided in a staged sequence across a timeline.
- Psychological First Aid is administered in the immediate aftermath of disaster.
- Crisis intervention strategies, enhanced interventions, and sustained therapy may be used for persons with severe and persistent distress and impairment.
- Medications may be prescribed on an individual basis according to specific clinical indications.

Source: ECHO

Introduction

As research on traumatized children and their families has increased, so has the level of thoughtfulness regarding psychosocial interventions to facilitate recovery. Early intervention in the aftermath of trauma is designed to reduce the initial distress and to foster adaptive coping for disaster survivors of all ages (NCTSN/NCPTSD, 2006). Effective intervention restores function and enhances recovery by providing Psychological First Aid; creating a safe and secure environment; reducing uncertainty, fear and anxiety; and mobilizing family and social supports. Scientific studies have begun to define the most effective interventions for use in the immediate aftermath of disaster and for sustaining long-term recovery.

General Intervention Principles

The following principles guide the selection and implementation of interventions for child survivors of traumatic experiences:

- Provide a sense of safety and security
- Connect the child with family and social supports
- Clarify reality and decrease uncertainty
- Provide opportunities for children to tell their stories
- Reconstruct the child's understanding of what occurred
- Determine the child's definition of the situation
- Identify and help correct cognitive distortions
- Assess the inventory of stressors the child is experiencing
- Assess for psychological and psychiatric disorders
- Promote and facilitate resiliency
- Provide carefully-guided and controlled re-exposure to the trauma as appropriate
- Clarify themes of guilt, betrayal, revenge, helplessness and excitement
- Assess the impact of the event on child development
- Work with changed attitudes toward self, others and the future
- Work with the loss of cherished beliefs
- Promote assimilation and integration of the traumatic experience

- Identify traumatic reminders
- Facilitate tolerance for disaster-related thoughts, feelings and moods
- Provide therapy for identified psychiatric disorders
- Facilitate the continued integrity of family and social support systems
- Promote adaptive coping

Colombia: children are often the first victims in conflicts situations 2005 © EC/ECHO/Susana Perez Diaz

Approaches to Intervention

Psychological interventions are sequenced and implemented over a timeline. Psychological First Aid (PFA) is appropriately provided in the immediate aftermath of disaster. As necessary, PFA may be followed by crisis intervention strategies and subsequently by more intensive and specialized therapeutic interventions. Depending on the scope of the disaster, community interventions may be implemented, possibly within a multi-faceted federal response. Psychoeducation and psychopharmacological interventions may be used at any point in the time-line as indicated. Early interventions should be carefully selected and employed only as necessary based upon accurate assessment of psychological indications (Figure 8.1).

Since disasters impact the individual child and have reverberating effects on the family and larger community, interventions must be tailored for application to the individual, the family unit and the encompassing community. This chapter is organized to present interventions at each of these three levels (Figure 8.2).

Figure 8.2

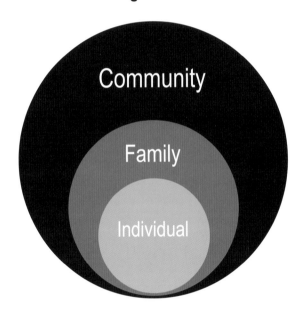

Figure 8.1

Some early interventions such as PFA can be provided by a wide range of disaster response professionals. Some responders are directly tasked with providing PFA or other forms of early psychosocial intervention as the primary focus of their job duties. However, most disaster professionals will continue to operate within their traditional emergency roles while simultaneously contributing to one or more of the "Core Actions" of PFA.

1. Individual Interventions

Psychological First Aid

Psychological First Aid is an evidence-informed early intervention for disaster survivors of all ages, and for response professionals, that can be applied in the immediate aftermath of disaster. Psychological First Aid is intended to reduce acute psychological distress, enhance resilience and foster adaptive coping (NCTSN/NCPTSD, 2006; Everly & Flynn, 2006). The conceptual origins of psychological first aid derive from diverse approaches for mitigating stress following trauma exposure such as crisis intervention, military psychiatry, disaster psychiatry, and trauma psychiatry (Lindemann, 1944; Mitchell, 1983; Pynoos & Nader, 1988; Ursano & Friedman, 2006).

Following September 11, 2001, the National Institute of Mental Health convened two expert consensus conferences to review the scientific research literature and recommend a comprehensive approach to early intervention following mass trauma (NIMH, 2002). The international expert panel recommended a multi-faceted approach that specified Psychological First Aid as one key component. Thereafter, federal funding was appropriated for the creation of a model Psychological First Aid intervention. The outcome of this expert-driven endeavor was the development of Psychological First Aid ("PFA") and the PFA Field Operations Guide was released concurrently with the federal response to Hurricane Katrina (NCTSN/NCPTSD, 2006). The two lead agencies that coordinated the development of PFA were the National Center for Child Traumatic Stress and the National Center for PTSD; thus, ensuring the applicability of this intervention to children and adolescents as well as adults of all ages.

The "five essential elements" of effective early intervention are those that move survivors upward in each of these domains (Reissman et al., 2006):

- From risk to safety
- From fear to calming
- From loss to connectedness
- From helplessness to efficacy
- From despair to hopefulness

Psychological First Aid (PFA) Field Operations Guide, 2nd Edition (NCTSN/NCPTSD, 2006)

Psychological First Aid (PFA) is an evidence-informed modular approach to help children, adolescents, adults and families in the immediate aftermath of disaster and terrorism. Psychological First Aid is designed to reduce the initial distress caused by traumatic events and to foster short- and long-term adaptive functioning and coping for disaster survivors in the acute phases of a disaster or mass casualty event. Principles and techniques of Psychological First Aid meet four basic standards. They are: (1) consistent with research evidence on risk and resilience following trauma; (2) applicable and practical in field settings; (3) appropriate for developmental levels across the lifespan; and (4) culturally informed and adaptable. Psychological First Aid does not assume that all survivors will develop severe mental health problems or long-term difficulties in recovery, but instead is based on an understanding that disaster survivors and others affected by such events will experience a broad range of early reactions (for example, physical, psychological, behavioral, spiritual). Some of these reactions will cause enough distress to interfere with adaptive coping, and may be alleviated by support from compassionate and caring disaster responders.

Psychological First Aid is designed for delivery by mental health and other disaster response workers who provide early assistance to affected children, families, and adults as part of an organized disaster response effort.

Psychological First Aid is a supportive intervention for use in the immediate aftermath of disasters, mass casualty events and terrorism. The suggested period of time to utilize these intervention strategies is days to weeks post event. If symptoms persist longer than a few weeks, a referral to more formal mental health services is recommended.

The goal of PFA is to facilitate the normal impetus of individuals to recover and to restore psychological equilibrium. PFA involves the employment of psychosocial supports to provide comfort, mitigate distress and physiological arousal. PFA providers reduce uncertainty by providing credible disaster event information regarding what has happened and what to expect.

Basic Objectives of Psychological First Aid

- Establish a human connection in a non-intrusive and compassionate manner
- Enhance immediate and ongoing safety
- Provide physical and emotional comfort
- Calm and orient emotionally overwhelmed and distraught survivors
- Encourage survivors to express their needs and concerns
- Provide information and practical assistance
- Connect with family and social supports
- Facilitate positive coping strategies and resiliency
- Link survivors with available services

Source: NCTSN/NCPTSD, 2006

Psychological First Aid is premised on the fact that disaster survivors will experience a spectrum of psychological reactions. While most will experience brief, transient distress, a smaller proportion will experience more enduring distress that interferes with adaptive functioning. Psychological First Aid assumes that relatively few disaster survivors will progress to severe impairment or psychiatric illness. Many survivors will need no formal early intervention. Nonetheless, almost all survivors will benefit from compassionate, available and non-intrusive care and support provided by disaster responders.

Survivors who are most likely to benefit from PFA participate are those with acute stress response symptoms and those with pre-existing risk factors that increase vulnerability to the disaster or traumatic event. While PFA may reduce distress in both adults and children, no evidence has shown that it will reduce the risk of subsequent psychological disorders. The PFA intervention facilitates recovery and does not intrude upon emotional processing, nor does it require elicitation of trauma narratives. Participation is voluntary on the part of survivors.

PFA providers are most effective when they approach disaster survivors with a calm, available "compassionate presence." In their interactions with disaster-affected children, PFA providers will comfort, educate, listen supportively and empathically and convey a sense of confidence that things are under control.

The modular format of PFA allows providers the flexibility to gather information from the survivor in order to customize the intervention to the survivor's specific situation. This differs markedly from earlier, regimented interventions that were applied using a "one size fits all" sequence of procedures.

When providing PFA, the initial tasks are to make contact with the child; provide life-sustaining safety, security, shelter, and sustenance (food, water, and clothing); and attend to basic comforts. As a high priority, PFA providers attempt to reunite the child with family members from whom they are separated.

Psychological First Aid (PFA) Core Actions

1. Contact and engagement
2. Safety and comfort
3. Stabilization
4. Information gathering: current needs and concerns
5. Practical assistance
6. Connection with social supports
7. Information on coping
8. Linkage with collaborative services

Source: NCTSN/NCPTSD, 2006

PFA "Core Actions" focus on restoring the child's and the families' adaptive coping capacities. Based on the information gathered in a non-intrusive manner, the PFA provider selects and tailors one or more Core Actions to the individual survivor. Among the Core Actions that may be selected, PFA providers may educate survivors about the effects of trauma and trauma reminders, normalize and validate distress responses, and identify available resources to aid recovery.

PFA attempts to facilitate the family's natural resiliency through reassurance, encouragement for positive coping behaviors, and mobilization of social support. By linking survivors to available, practical resources, PFA encourages survivors to take constructive actions toward rapid recovery from disaster and to resume normal routines as quickly as possible.

It is essential that PFA providers observe and identify adults and children who are judged to be at elevated psychological risk and may require more selective professional attention and support. Children at risk who might benefit from crisis intervention are those who manifest hyperarousal, intense anxiety, disorientation, psychological numbness, regressive behaviors, grief reactions and dissociative responses. Providers identify specific disaster stressors the child has experienced. It is important to assess which children have been personally physically or have family members who were injured or killed, those who have been separated from loved ones, and those who lost their homes or valued personal possessions. Clinicians also ascertain the child's pre-disaster level of functioning for comparison with the child's current capacities to help decide whether further professional attention is indicated.

Psychoeducation

"Psychoeducation" is an intervention which informs persons about the effects of trauma exposure, bereavement, risk and protective factors, coping strategies, problem-solving skills and stress management techniques. Psychoeducation is beneficial for most survivors, carries little stigma and can be delivered either informally or in formal structured presentations (Gard & Ruzek, 2006). The goal is to normalize disaster reactions, increase the survivor's sense of control, help families recognize situations requiring further evaluation or intervention, encourage children and families to identify and use social supports,

and promote adaptive coping (Gard & Ruzek 2006; Young 2006). Psychoeducation can be reassuring for parents by increasing their confidence in their own parenting skills and providing specific guidance on how to support their children (Cohen et al., 2006b). Psychoeducation is an ongoing process throughout all the stages of recovery from trauma exposure.

Parents may need assistance in understanding how to talk with their children about traumatic events. Parents are encouraged to listen to their child's story of what happened, respecting the child's expression of fears and anxieties. Ideally, parents will be honest in their communications, create a safe environment, empathize with their children, provide reassurance and hopeful expectations and be supportive and understanding when children briefly regress in their behaviors after exposure to a disaster. Parents are able to encourage children's natural tendency to attempt to master the disaster experience and allow expression of emotions such as anger, anxiety and unhappy feelings. Parents should encourage children to ask questions; consider sharing their own feelings; serve as a role model for managing emotions; and maintain household routines around work, eating, sleeping and recreation.

Parents can help their children identify trustworthy and dependable community helpers such as police, firefighters and emergency personnel, and can provide children with emergency numbers and guidance on how to access help. Parents and caretakers are encouraged to minimize children's exposure to traumatic reminders such as situations, activities or locations that trigger memories of the disaster. Parents should limit television viewing. When children do watch television coverage of the disaster, parents should attend and be ready to answer questions.

Psychoeducation for Parents

- **GATHER TOGETHER AS A FAMILY.** The best safeguard against disaster stress is the love and support of family members.

- **REASSURE THE CHILD THAT HE OR SHE IS SAFE.** Let children know the family will be safe and will stay together.

- **RECOGNIZE THAT CHILDREN ARE CHILDREN.** Younger children may not be able to verbalize their fears and anxieties. When they are afraid, they are most fearful of being left alone. Be sure to include them in your activities before and after an anticipated disaster such as a hurricane.

- **TALK TO YOU CHILD IN LANGUAGE THAT HE OR SHE CAN UNDERSTAND.** Explain to your child what happened, what is happening and what is going to happen in a language that he or she can understand.

- **LISTEN TO YOUR CHILD'S THOUGHTS.** Try to understand how your child thinks and how he/she explains what has happened. Listen and answer questions honestly, but do not volunteer more information than they need or are prepared to hear.

- **LISTEN TO YOUR CHILD'S FEELINGS.** Listen continuously and reassure children who are afraid. Try not to minimize or ignore their feelings. Where possible join with your child in understanding their feelings, but in a way that conveys that you will manage the situation. Allow your children to mourn or grieve over a lost toy, a missing blanket and the loss or damage to your home.

- **ENCOURAGE CHILDREN TO TALK.** Provide an atmosphere of acceptance in which children feel free to express their anxieties. Include family, friends or other children in the discussions. Another way of communicating is to have children draw pictures of the events surrounding the disaster. Have the child tell you about their drawings.

- **ROUTINIZE AND NORMALIZE YOUR CHILD'S LIFE.** Get back to a routine as quickly as possible. This signifies to your children that you are maintaining control, another sign of adaptive coping. Observing regular meal schedules, planning calming pre-bedtime activities and reinstating a bedtime will revitalize family structure and help provide a sense of security for your children.

- **REGULATE EXPOSURE TO DISASTER IMAGERY.** Limit your child's exposure to the imagery associated with the disaster (television news, newspapers, gratuitous violence, injury and death). Avoid situations and traumatic reminders that bring back your child's fears.

Psychological Debriefing

There is no evidence in the psychiatric literature to support a policy of a formal single session therapeutic intervention for all survivors of a traumatic event (Bisson et al., 2007). Serious questions have been raised regarding the efficacy of psychological debriefing as well as the risk of potential harm for some recipients (Bisson et al., 2007). There is little empirical data on psychological debriefing with children, particularly those who have experienced a disaster. Most experts have concluded that no empirical evidence exists to support the use of intensive emotional processing, a hallmark of psychological debriefing, in the immediate aftermath of trauma exposure (Orner et al., 2006).

Psychopharmacological Intervention

Psychological reactions to disasters vary from brief psychological distress, which frequently improves without intervention, to more enduring posttraumatic anxiety symptoms that may lead to diagnosed PTSD and other mental disorders. A survey of the adolescent population has estimated that lifetime prevalence of PTSD is six percent (Giaconia et. al., 1995). Little empirical evidence exists, however, to support the use of psychotropic medications for PTSD in children and adolescents.

Donnelly et al. (1999) suggest that children with PTSD are more likely to manifest additional psychiatric conditions such as depression (Giaconia et al., 1995; Sack et al., 1995); anxiety disorders (Kinzie et al., 1986; Giaconia et al., 1995); and disruptive behaviors such as attention deficit hyperactivity disorder, conduct disorder, substance abuse and oppositional defiant disorder (Steiner et al., 1997; McLeer et al., 1998). It is often the presence of co-existing psychiatric disorders that require psychopharmacological intervention. Few controlled studies of psychotropic drugs in children exist (Baldwin et al., 2005). Psychopharmacologic interventions are not generally used with children following disaster except in those instances when the clinical presentation is severe or there is evidence of other simultaneous psychiatric conditions that warrant intervention.

The use of psychotropic medications in children should focus on target symptoms such as agitation, aggressive behaviors, anxiety and depression when they impair the child's capacities to meet the ordinary demands of everyday life.

Adult studies have demonstrated the efficacy of using several classes of medications to treat PTSD including selective serotonin reuptake inhibitors (SSRIs), tricyclics, alpha-2 agonists, monoamine oxidase inhibitors (MAOIs) and beta-blockers (Foa et al., 2000; van der Kolk, 2001; Baldwin et al., 2005). The United Kingdom Committee on Safety of Medicines has suggested that the use of SSRIs is generally acceptable for the treatment of anxiety

disorders because the risk of self-harm is minimal and the therapeutic benefits are well-documented (Baldwin et al., 2005). The use of benzodiazepines, while they may reduce distress and promote sleep, do not improve PTSD nor alter the progress of the psychological reactions to trauma over time (van der Kolk, 2001).

Specific Crisis Intervention Strategies

A "crisis" involves an acute disruption of psychological equilibrium. The elements that combine to precipitate a "crisis" are exposure to a traumatic or hazardous event coupled with the perception that this event is the cause of distress or disruption that is not easily resolved through the usual coping mechanisms. Crisis intervention is a strategy for reducing or eliminating specific symptoms with the intent of restoring disaster survivors to their pre-crisis level of functioning. Specific attention should be given to extreme acute stress reactions such as intense anxiety, depressed mood, anger or hyperarousal which interferes with coping; dissociative symptoms such as derealization, depersonalization and frozen emotionality; bodily symptoms; disturbed sleep; and impaired cognitive processing including decreased concentration, confusion and poor decision-making (Young, 2006).

Crisis intervention is a brief psychotherapy usually presented in one to six sessions. Specific crisis intervention techniques include the use of relaxation exercises such as slow breathing, muscle relaxation and guided imagery; cognitive reframing; and psychoeducation about expectable responses to trauma, positive and negative coping, and problem-solving strategies. Stress management approaches may include distraction techniques such as participating in social activities, play or watching television. As much as possible, the mental health professional normalizes the child's psychological response to the traumatic event. In a supportive manner, the therapist allows the child to tell his/her story, but doesn't interrogate or press for reactions. The therapist actively promotes recreation and physical activities such as exercise, sports and dance; healthful diet and sleep patterns; social interactions with loved ones; and productive task or work experiences. The therapist also discourages the use of alcohol or drugs, social isolation, and excessive work. Crisis intervention has been shown to be efficacious in restoring pre-disaster functioning for both adults and youth (Koss & Butcher, 1986; Auerbach & Kilmann, 1977; Goenjian, et. al., 1997).

Sustained Psychological Interventions

Children and family members with sustained posttraumatic stress symptoms, mood disorder, disruptive behaviors, dissociation, traumatic bereavement, and bodily symptoms may not respond to crisis intervention. While most children experience anxiety following a disaster, many also need an intervention that is sensitive to the spectrum of posttraumatic stress symptoms as well as any co-existing mental disorders. There is empirical evidence that psychotherapy is efficacious but more research is required before we fully understand the mechanisms that lead to change. Most empirical studies of psychotherapy have focused on brief cognitive behavioral therapies as they have been more readily manualized for research purposes. The mainstream psychosocial approaches are psychodynamic in nature and usually involve play therapy, family interventions and group therapies. While less utilized, cognitive behavioral therapy has the most empirical evidence to support its use.

Cognitive Behavioral Therapy (CBT):
Trauma-Focused Cognitive Behavioral Therapy (TF-CBT) and cognitive behavioral interventions have been found to be efficacious for use with trauma survivors (Cohen et al, 2006a). Cognitive behavioral interventions have been employed in both individual and group formats in various community and school programs, usually over a 10-16 week period. CBT approaches include providing information about predictable and expected responses to trauma; engaging children in exercises to identify and appropriately express emotions; practicing anxiety reduction techniques

such as relaxation, focused breathing, positive self-talk and thought-stopping; discovering the relationship between thoughts, feelings and behaviors (cognitive restructuring); and guiding children through "titrated re-exposure" using trauma narratives, story-telling, poems, and drawings to help the child slowly achieve mastery over the traumatic situation (Cohen et al, 2006a). Cognitive processing of the event helps the child to examine and correct misperceptions and distortions. Reconstructing the trauma experience is an integral aspect of processing the event. The goal is to desensitize the child to the trauma event and traumatic reminders so the child can integrate the trauma into his or her life (Cohen et al. 2006a). This can be done verbally, in writing or in the context of art or play. A modification of CBT has been developed for childhood traumatic grief following the loss of a loved one (Cohen et al., 2006a).

In one study, 24 children, ages 8-18 years, who had experienced a single-incident traumatic event, were randomly assigned to a 10-week CBT intervention or to a wait-list control condition (Smith et al., 2007). At the 6-month follow-up, only one child in the CBT group continued to meet criteria for PTSD compared with 60 percent of children in the control group. CBT subjects also experienced improved function and significant reductions in anxiety and depression.

Cognitive-Behavioral Therapies

- Psychoeducation
- Parenting skills
- Anxiety management techniques
- Affect modulation
- Cognitive restructuring
- Exposure therapies
- Emotional/ information processing therapies
- Conjoint child and family sessions
- Enhancing safety and future developmental trajectory

Source: Bisson and Cohen, 2006

Play Therapy:

Play has been defined as the child's version of the human ability to deal with experience by creating model situations and mastering reality by experimentation (Erikson, 1963). Play is fantasy woven around objects. Play activity has been described as pretend, imaginative, dramatic, spontaneous, self-generated and an end in itself (Fein, 1981). In play, the child's innermost conflicts, concerns and fears are expressed. Wish fulfillment, expression of pent-up emotions, and experimentation, or "trial action", are employed as the child turns passive into active and creates in fantasy what was often absent in reality—ways of mastering trauma (American Academy of Child and Adolescent Psychiatry, 2004). Fein (1981) describes several childhood activities that meet the criteria of pretend play: 1) familiar activities are performed in the absence of necessary equipment, 2) activities are not carried to their usual outcome, 3) inanimate objects are treated as if they are animate and 4) the child performs an activity usually performed by an adult.

Play therapy focuses on understanding the meaning that the child places on the traumatic experience. Play therapy explores how the trauma experience relates to other childhood experiences, prior traumatic exposures, internal conflicts, defense mechanisms and coping strategies (American Academy of Child and Adolescent Psychiatry, 2007). Through play, the child may relive and repeat the traumatic situation in fantasy but bring it to a different resolution with a sense of empowerment and mastery (Gillis, 1993). After the Chowchilla bus kidnapping, children played games in which kidnapping occurred and the children in fantasy triumphed over the kidnappers, turning anxiety into mastery (Terr, 1981). As reenacted in traumatic play, the child may deal with the shattering loss of such cherished childhood beliefs such as: goodness will triumph over evil, people are inherently good, parents are powerful and can always provide for and protect the child, and children are invulnerable to injury and death (Shaw, 2000).

The therapist interprets the child's thoughts and actions exhibited through play, helping the child deal with feelings of helplessness experienced during the disaster, integrating the trauma into the child's life experiences and offering the child new coping strategies (Terr, 1981). Through the use of play activities, children learn to distinguish adaptive and maladaptive coping, enhance resiliency, increase self-awareness of internal emotional states and learn empowerment strategies. In some instances the symbolic repetition of the traumatic situation may result in relief of anxiety as the treatment scenario is mastered; and in other instances the anxiety may continue unabated (Terr, 1981). The therapist must know when to allow the child to freely express emotions related to the traumatic event and when to clarify meaning, label emotions and interpret what is being played out. Play therapy has been shown to provide significant clinical improvement for about 75 percent of children who are treated (Target & Fonagy 1994a,b, 1997).

Guided activity coloring workbooks have been developed for younger children, families and teachers that allow children to move at their own pace to achieve mastery over traumatic events with adult assistance. Kliman et al. (2001) developed such a manual, *My Book about War and Terrorism,* which allows the child to describe memories, perceptions and fears, and to evolve positive coping strategies.

Source: FEMA Photo Library

2. Family Interventions

When possible, the traumatized child is treated in conjunction with family members. The effect of the traumatic stressor on the family influences the child's psychological response, while the child's response in turn impacts the family's adaptation to trauma. The family reaction to a traumatic event is shaped by the nature of the stressors and the reactions of individual family members, mediated by the family's religious, ethnic and cultural beliefs. As a caretaking unit for the child, the family is challenged by its experience of traumatic exposure, death and separation from loved ones. Family and parental support can mitigate the child's risk for developing posttraumatic stress symptoms. Conversely, the presence of poor family functioning, or parents with psychological disorders, predicts elevated levels of psychological disorders in the children (American Academy of Child and Adolescent Psychiatry, 1998).

The efficacy of family interventions following trauma exposure remains to be proven (Miller, 2003). Several studies that have attempted to supplement child-focused CBT for anxiety disorders with family CBT have not convincingly demonstrated incremental efficacy for the family component (Barrett et al., 1996; Cobham et al., 1998; Spence et al., 2000). However, Wood et al. (2006) compared child-focused CBT with family-focused CBT (12-16 sessions) for children, ages 6-13 years, with anxiety disorders (no PTSD) and found that the family CBT approach was associated with decreased severity of the anxiety disorder coupled with improved social and school functioning.

Berkowitz and Marans (2006) developed the Child and Family Traumatic Stress Intervention (CFTSI), a brief therapy designed for families with children, ages 7-18 years, that is implemented in the wake of trauma exposure. Four sessions of CFTSI are delivered in the family home or in an office setting. CFTSI involves extensive reporting on symptoms and feelings. CFTSI is intended to decrease the negative impact of children's exposure to traumatic events and serves concurrently as an assessment and engagement strategy as well as a secondary prevention intervention. The goals of the CFTSI are to prevent a child from developing posttraumatic symptoms and to increase the likelihood that children will actively engage and sustain participation in longer-term treatments when these are indicated. CFTSI seeks to enhance family communication and support for the trauma-exposed child through the following approaches:

1. Increasing the level of understanding of the impact of trauma exposure on symptoms, behavior changes and daily functioning
2. Increasing the child's ability to communicate feelings and symptoms to the parent
3. Increasing parents' ability to respond appropriately and supportively to the child's difficulties by teaching parents strategies to use with their child
4. Providing case management and care coordination related to trauma exposure
5. Helping the family access needed services and maintain parents' focus on their children rather than on the external stressors associated with the traumatic event

3. Community Interventions

Social Support:

Social support has been defined as the "social interactions that provide individuals with actual assistance and embed them into a web of social relationships perceived to be loving, caring and readily available in times of need" (Kaniasty, 2005). The presence of strong and available social support has been documented to mitigate both acute and long-term mental health effects of trauma (Kaniasty, 2005; Pine & Cohen, 2002). Beyond the family sphere, children's development is influenced by continuous interaction with peers, teachers, community members and mass media. Through social interaction, children internalize culturally-constructed norms, values and beliefs, including modes of expressing emotion and acceptable social behavior. Children's development is inextricably connected to the social and cultural influences that surround them, particularly the families and communities that function as children's "life-support systems."

Using available social supports is a helpful strategy in a community-based shelter or disaster recovery setting. If individuals are disconnected from their usual sources of social support, they should be encouraged to make use of immediately available options (the disaster responder, health care professionals, relief workers, other survivors in the shelter environment), while being respectful of individual preferences (NCCTS/NCPTSD, 2006).

Systems of Care:

Community-based interventions following disaster involve setting up a "system of care" for the benefit of children and their families (AACAP Parameter, 2007). "System of Care" refers to a comprehensive network of mental health services, child-serving programs and natural community support services organized to meet the needs of children and families. Ursano and Friedman (2006) have suggested that disaster mental health care requires a systematic approach that integrates a community-level public health focus with an individualized clinical treatment focus. Systems of care represent an organized effort to integrate government, community and school-based services that are sensitive to the needs of the family, individualized to meet the child's needs and delivered in the least restrictive environment.

School-Based Interventions:

One of the most effective and expeditious "interventions" for child survivors of disaster is rapid restoration of an operating school system. A school-based behavioral health response plan should include assessment strategies to identify children at risk and to distinguish whether these children can be managed in the school setting or require referral to community mental health professionals. Subsequent to disaster, intervention teams composed of mental health professionals and crisis intervention specialists are formed and assigned to specific schools or regions to assist the school in assessment and intervention programs. In the school community, it is essential to address the emotional needs of teachers, counselors and school administrators who not only interact daily with the disaster-affected children and their families, but frequently are themselves survivors of the same disaster.

Source: FEMA Photo Library

The school system is often staffed with counselors and crisis intervention specialists who identify children at risk and intervene when necessary on behalf of children and their families. For example, 58 percent of children seen for counseling after September 11 were managed in the school setting (Stuber et al., 2002). Schools can implement programs and create opportunities for children to connect with each other and share their experiences. In addition, schools provide routine academic tasks requiring focused attention, and opportunities for success experiences that help facilitate resiliency and recovery. Post-disaster, schools disseminate accurate disaster recovery information, provide health care for school-aged youth and distribute life-sustaining supplies. Group CBT strategies have been designed for implementation in schools (Cohen et al., 2006).

Community Resilience: Resilience is a measure of the rapidity and efficacy with which a community recovers from disaster. For a community to be resilient, its members must work together to quickly take effective actions to respond to emerging adversities. The best contribution to the resiliency of a community is preparation and anticipation of the consequences of disaster. If residents, agencies and organizations take meaningful and intentional actions before an event, they can help the community reestablish stability after the event. Resilience implies that after an event, a community may not only be able to cope and to recover, but that it may also change to reflect different priorities arising from the disaster. To be most effective, community plans must address the emotional well being of residents, families and their children. NCTSN has put together a guidebook that provides information about building community resilience aimed at helping communities improve their capacity to respond effectively to natural or man-made disasters or acts of terrorism (Gurwitch et al., 2007).

The Federal Response: The federal government is responsible for a number of initiatives and programs that are designed to provide relief to the survivors of disaster. The Disaster Relief Act of 1974 established the Federal Emergency Management Agency (FEMA) to have responsibility for coordinating the federal response. In 2003, FEMA became a part of the newly-formed Department of Homeland Security. Federal involvement occurs after a major disaster has overwhelmed local resources and the state requests such assistance. Once the President declares a major disaster, a federal-state agreement is drawn up delineating the types of assistance to be provided and the areas eligible for assistance. Programs are initiated to provide support for individuals experiencing mild to moderate psychological stress and to facilitate recovery. The Secretary of the Department of Homeland Security appoints a Principal Federal Official (PFO), who oversees the disaster response including local, state and federal governmental disaster resources and coordination

with voluntary disaster relief agencies such as the Red Cross or Salvation Army.

Disaster mental health services are provided through the Disaster Branch of the Center for Mental Health Services (CMHS) within the Substance Abuse and Mental Health Services Administration (SAMHSA). The Stafford Act provides funding for training and services to implement psychological services. Two types of grants are provided by FEMA through the Center of Mental Health Services: 1) Immediate Services Programs providing screening, diagnostic and counseling outreach services for up to 60 days, and 2) Regular Services which funds crisis counseling, community outreach and consultation to assist people affected by disaster. The network of public and private community mental health centers and academic institutions provides education and training to crisis intervention specialists who are mobilized at times of disaster.

The American Red Cross, an independent humanitarian organization, is privately funded and mandated by Congress to have a central and unique role in disaster response. The American Red Cross provides designated "mass care" venues for disaster survivors where psychosocial interventions can be implemented, along with psychoeducation.

Federal Response to Terrorism: The Federal Bureau of Investigation (FBI) has the primary responsibility to direct the response to terrorism, spearheading the "crisis management" of the event. "Consequence management" includes measures to protect public health and safety, restore essential government services and provide emergency relief to government, businesses and individuals affected by the terrorist act (Siegrist & Graham, 2000). The Department of Health and Human Services assumes major responsibility for the medical, public health and mental health emergency support activities, including coordination with state and local governments in providing resources to the community.

Summary

As research on traumatized children and their families has increased there has been growing interest in defining and promulgating evidence-based interventions. Empirically-based studies have begun to distinguish which interventions are most helpful in the immediate aftermath of disaster and which may be most efficacious for sustained recovery. Psychosocial interventions occur across a time-line. Psychological First Aid is administered in the immediate aftermath of disaster, and is followed by more focused crisis intervention strategies as needed. If continuing assessment documents persistent distress and emerging psychological morbidity, then sustained therapeutic interventions are employed. Psychopharmacological interventions may be used at any time according to specific clinical indications.

Generally Accepted Truths

Generally-Accepted Truths: The Psychological Effects of Trauma on Children

Children's response to stressful situations is often less intense than might be anticipated.

The child's psychological response to trauma varies with age and cognitive development.

There is a commonality of psychological responses to trauma regardless of the specific trauma exposure.

Exposure to a traumatic stressor may occur through direct and immediate physical impact, witnessing the event on-scene, media exposure or interpersonal connectedness to disaster victims.

Combined forms of exposure increase risks for psychological consequences.

Repetitive exposure to a "distant" trauma such as television and media viewing increases children's risks for posttraumatic stress symptoms.

Exposure to human-generated trauma and disaster is associated with increased risk for psychological impairment and illness compared with exposure to natural disasters.

An "acute trauma" refers to a traumatic event that is circumscribed in time and space. A "chronic trauma" refers to a traumatic situation in which there is continuing and unrelenting exposure to an inventory of primary and secondary stressors.

A disaster or extreme event may set in motion a cascade of secondary stressors—ongoing hardships and adversities--that effectively transduce an acute ("event") trauma into a chronic ("process") trauma.

Complex trauma refers to the exposure to violence that begins in childhood and is repeated throughout the developmental years. The consequences of complex trauma exposure include difficulties with emotional control, mood instability, interpersonal and social difficulties and diminished self-efficacy. These consequences increase the child's vulnerability to future trauma.

Trauma impacts not just the individual child but also the family and social system within which the child lives.

The family environment, the parent's level of function and the parent's symptoms predict the possible expression of posttraumatic stress symptoms in children.

The child's subjective experience of the traumatic situation at the time of exposure is a powerful predictor of the child's psychological outcome.

Previous trauma exposure increases vulnerability to subsequent trauma exposure.

Being physically injured, or having a family member injured or killed, increases the risk of posttraumatic stress symptoms for both children and adults.

The psychological response to a traumatic situation may be delayed ("sleeper effect") and may increase over time.

Traumatic reminders are internal and external triggers that suddenly bring the traumatic event back into awareness with alls its emotional, perceptual and ideational content; creating an ongoing risk for psychological distress.

War is characterized by chronic and enduring exposure to trauma-related events for children and families. The greater the dose and intensity of war-related trauma exposure, the greater is the likelihood of psychological symptoms.

The psychological effects of earlier trauma exposure in childhood add to the child's current psychological/psychiatric syndromes.

Cognitive behavioral intervention techniques have the greatest empirical evidence regarding efficacy for treating posttraumatic stress symptoms for persons exposed to trauma and disaster.

The existence of community solidarity and social cohesion before and after disaster favorably affects the course of posttraumatic stress symptoms.

REFERENCES

References

Achenbach TM, Verhulst FC, Edelbrock C, Baron GD, Akkerhuis GW (1987). Epidemiological comparisons of American and Dutch children: II. Behavioral/emotional problems reported by teachers for ages 6 to 11. Journal of the American Academy of Child and Adolescent Psychiatry, 26(3):326-32.

Ahearn FL, Cohen RE (Eds.) (1985). Disasters and Mental Health: An Annotated Bibliography (DHHS Publication No. ADM 84-1311). Rockville, MD: Center for Mental Health Services.

Alexander JB (2001). Operational lethality. Harvard International Review, XXIII(2):64-69.

Alexander JC, Eyerman R, Giesen B, Smelser NJ, Sztomka P (2004). Cultural Trauma and Collective Identity. Berkeley CA: University of California Press.

Almqvist K, Broberg AG (1999). Mental health and social adjustment in young refugee children 3 1/2 years after their arrival in Sweden. Journal of the American Academy of Child and Adolescent Psychiatry, 38(6):723-30.

American Academy of Child and Adolescent Psychiatry (AACAP) (1998). Posttraumatic stress disorder in children and adolescents, Journal of the American Academy of Child and Adolescent Psychiatry, 37: Supp. 10.

American Academy of Child and Adolescent Psychiatry (AACAP) (2004, in press). Practice Parameter for Psychodynamic Psychotherapy of Children. Kernberg PF (Principal author), Journal of the American Academy of Child and Adolescent Psychiatry (in press).

American Academy of Child and Adolescent Psychiatry (AACAP) (2007, in press). Practice Parameter for the Assessment and Treatment of Children and Adolescents with Posttraumatic Stress Disorder. Journal of the American Academy of Child and Adolescent Psychiatry (in press).

American Psychiatric Association (1994). Diagnostic and Statistical Manual of Mental Disorders, Fourth Edition. Washington DC: American Psychiatric Association.

American Psychiatric Association (2007). Special Populations. Available at http://www.psych.org/disaster/dpc_populations.cfm

Auerbach SM, Kilmann PR (1977). Crisis intervention: A review of outcomes research. Psychological Bulletin, 84:1189-1217.

Balaban V (2006). Psychological assessment of children in disasters and emergencies. Disasters, 30(2):178-198.

Baldwin DS, Anderson IM, Nutt DJ, Bandelow B, Bond, A. Davidson JR, den Boer JA, Fineberg NA, Knapp M., Scott J, Wittchen HU (2005). Evidence-based guidelines for the pharmacological treatment of anxiety disorders: recommendations from the British Association of Psychopharmacology. Journal of Psychopharmacology, 19(6):567-596.

Barrett PM, Dadds MR, Rapee RM (1996). Family treatment of childhood anxiety: a controlled study. Journal of Consulting and Clinical Psychology, 64(2):333-342.

Bayer CP, Klasen F, Adam H (2007). Association of trauma and PTSD symptoms with openness to reconciliation and feelings of revenge among former Ugandan and Congolese child soldiers. Journal of the American Medical Association, 298(5):555-559.

Bayer CP, Klasen F, Adam H (2007).Trauma and PTSD in former Ugandan and Congolese child soldiers associated with openness to reconciliation and feelings of revenge. Journal of the American Medical Association, 298(5):479-4871.

Berkowitz S, Marans S (2006). Child and Family Traumatic Stress Intervention. National Childhood Traumatic Stress Network, National Center for Children Exposed to Violence.

Bisson JI, Brayne M, Ochberg FM, Everly GS (2007). Early psychosocial intervention following traumatic events. American Journal of Psychiatry, 164(7):1016-1019.

Bisson JI, Cohen JA (2006). Disseminating early interventions following trauma. Journal of Traumatic Stress, 19(5):583-95.

Black D, Urbanowicz MA (1987). Family intervention with bereaved children. Journal of Child Psychology and Psychiatry, 28(3):467-76.

Bloch D, Silber E, Perry S (1956). Some factors in the emotional reactions of children to disaster. American Journal of Psychiatry, 113: 416-422.

Bostic JQ, King RA (2007). Clinical assessment of children and adolescents: Content and structure. In: Martin A, Volkmar FR (Eds.), Lewis's Child and Adolescent Psychiatry (pp. 323-344). Philadelphia: Wolters Kluwer.

Boyle MH, Lipman EL (2002). Do places matter? Socioeconomic disadvantage and behavioral problems of children in Canada. Journal of Consulting and Clinical Psychology, 70(2):378-389.

Breier A, Kelsoe JR, Kirwin PD, Beller SA, Wollkowitz OM, Pickar D (1988). Early parental loss and development of adult psychopathology. Archives of General Psychiatry, 45:987-993.

Breslau N, Davis GC, Andreski P, Peterson E (1991).Traumatic events and posttraumatic stress disorder in an urban population of young adults. Archives of General Psychiatry, 48(3):216-22.

Breslau N, Kessler RC, Chilcoat HD, Schultz LR, Davis GC, Andreski P (1998). Trauma and posttraumatic stress disorder in the community: The 1996 Detroit Area Survey of Trauma. Archives of General Psychiatry, 55(7):626-32.

Brooks-Gunn J, Duncan GJ (1997). The effects of poverty on children. The Future of Children, 7(2):55-71.

Cantor NF (2001). In The Wake of the Plague. New York: The Free Press.

Cobham VE, Dadds MR, Spence SH (1998). The role of parental anxiety in the treatment of childhood anxiety. Journal of Consulting and Clinical Psychology, 66(6):893-905.

Cohen JA (1998). (Principal Author) Practice Parameter For The Assessment And Treatment of Children and Adolescents with Posttrauamtic Stress Disorder. Journal of the American Academy of Child and Adolescent Psychiatry 37(10):4S-26S.

Cohen JA, Mannarino AP, Gibson LE, Cozza SJ, Brymer MJ, Murray L (2006b). Interventions for children and adolescents following disaster. In: Ritchie EC, Watson PJ, Friedman MJ (Eds.), Interventions following Mass Violence and Disasters (pp. 227-256). New York: Guilford Press.

Cohen JA, Mannarino AP, Staron VR (2006a). A pilot study of modified cognitive behavioral therapy for childhood traumatic grief. Journal of the American Academy of Child and Adolescent Psychiatry, 45(912):1465-1473.

Cooper NS, Feder A, Southwick AM, Charney DS (2007). Resiliency and vulnerability to trauma. In Romer D & Walker EF (Eds.), Adolescent Psychopathology and the Developing Brain. Oxford UK: Oxford University Press.

Copeland WE, Keeler G, Angold A, Costello EJ (2007). Traumatic events and posttraumatic stress in childhood. Archives of General Psychiatry, 64(5):577-84.

Cordasco KM, Eisenman DP, Glik DC, Golden JF, Asch SM (2007). They blew the levee: Distrust of authorities among Hurricane Katrina evacuees. Journal of Health Care for the Poor and Underserved, 18(2): 277-282.

Costello EJ, Compton SN, Keeler G, Angold A (2003). Relationships between poverty and psychopathology: A natural experiment. Journal of the American Medical Association, 290(15):2023-2029.

Costello EJ, Erkanli A, Fairbank JA, Angold A (2002). The prevalence of potentially traumatic events in childhood and adolescence. Journal of Traumatic Stress, 15(2):99-112.

Covell NH, Allen G, Foster MJ, Essock SM, Pease EA, Felton CJ ,Lanzara CB, Donahue SA (2006). Service utilization and event reaction patterns among children who received Project Liberty Counseling. Psychiatric Services, 57(9):1277-1282.

CRED: Centre for Research on the Epidemiology of Disasters (2006). EM-DAT—Emergency Management Database: Disaster List. Universitaires de Louvain, Louvain-La-Neuve, Belgium. Available at: http://www.em-dat.net/

Culpepper RC (2001). Agents of bioterrorism. In Planning For Bioterrorism: Behaviors and Mental Health Response to Weapons of Mass Destruction and Mass Disruption. Center for the Study of Traumatic Stress, Department of Psychiatry, Uniformed Services University of the Health Sciences, Bethesda, Maryland.

Curtis A, Mills JW, Leitner M (2007). Katrina and vulnerability: The geography of stress.
Journal of Health Care for the Poor and Underserved, 18(2):315-330.

Cuttler S (2005). The Geography of Social Vulnerability: Race, Class, and Catastrophe. Available at http://understandingkatrina.ssrc.org/Cutter/

De Bellis MD, Baum AS, Birmaher B, Keshavan MS, Eccard CH, Boring AM, Jenkins FJ, Ryan ND (1999a). A.E. Bennett Research Award. Developmental traumatology. Part I: Biological stress systems. Biological Psychiatry, 45(10):1259-1270.

De Bellis MD, Keshavan MS, Clark DB, Casey BJ, Giedd JN, Boring AM, Frustaci K, Ryan ND (1999b). A.E. Bennett Research Award. Developmental traumatology. Part II: Brain development. Biological Psychiatry, 45(10):1271-1284.

de Jong J (2002). Trauma, War and Violence. Public Mental Health in Socio-Cultural Context. Kluver Academic/Plenum Publishers, New York.

De Lisi LE, Maurizio A, Yost M, Papparozzi CF, Fulchino C, Katz CL, Altesman J, Biel M, Lee J, Stevens P (2003). A survey of New Yorkers after the Sept. 11, 2001, terrorist attacks. American Journal of Psychiatry, 160(4):780-783.

De Silva DGH, Hobbs CJ (2001). Conscription of children in armed conflict. British Medical Journal, 322(7298): 1372.doi: 1010.1136/bmj.322.7298.1372.

Doctors Without Borders (MSF) (2005). Psychosocial and Mental Health Interventions in Areas of Mass Violence. Available at http://www.medicisenzafrontiere.it/editoriale/MSF_mentalhealthguidelines.pdf

Dolan MA, Krug SE (2006). Pediatric disaster preparedness in the wake of Katrina: Lessons to be learned. Clinical Pediatric Emergency Medicine, 7(1):59–66.

Donnelly CL, Amaya-Jackson L, March J (1999). Psychopharmacology of pediatric posttraumatic stress disorder, Journal of the American Academy of Child and Adolescent Psychiatry, 9(3):203-20.

Dowdney L (2000). Annotation: Childhood Bereavement following parental death. Journal of Child Psychology and Psychiatry and Allied Disciplines, 41(7): 819-830.

Duncan J, Arntson L (2004). Children in Crisis: Good Practices in Evaluating Psychosocial Programming. Save the Children Federation, Inc. Available at http://www.savethechildren.org/publications/technical-resources/emergencies-protection/Good_Practices_in_Evaluating_Psychosocial_Programming.pdf

Duncan GJ, Brooks-Gunn J, Klebanov PK (1994). Economic deprivation and early childhood development. Child Development, 65(2):296-318.

Durant W, Durant A (1968). The Lessons of History. New York: Simon & Schuster.

Elizur E, Kaffman M (1982). Children's bereavement reactions following death of the father. Journal of the American Academy of Child and Adolescent Psychiatry, 21(5):474-480.

Elizur E, Kaffman M (1983). Factors Influencing the severity of childhood bereavement reactions. American Journal of Orthopsychiatry, 53(4):668-676.

Erikson E (1963). Childhood and Society, Second edition. New York: Norton.

Erikson K (1976). Disaster at Buffalo Creek: Loss of communality at Buffalo Creek. American Journal of Psychiatry, 133:302-305.

Everly GS Jr, Flynn BW (2006). Principles and practical procedures for acute psychological first aid training for personnel without mental health experience. International Journal of Emergency Mental Health, 8(2):93-100.

Fein GF (1981). Pretend play in childhood: An integrative review. Child Development, 52: 1095-1118.

Finch AJ, Daugherty TK (1993). Issues in the assessment of post-traumatic stress disorder in children. In: Saylor CF (Ed.), Children and Disasters (pp.45-66). New York: Plenum Press.

Flynn BW (2006). Meeting the Needs of Special Populations in Disasters and Emergencies: Making It Work in Rural Areas. Presented at: National Association for Rural Mental Health, San Antonio TX, August 22, 2006.

Foa EB, Cahill SP, Boscarino JA, Hobfoll SE, Lahad M, McNally RJ, Solomon Z (2005). Social, psychological, and psychiatric interventions following terrorist attacks: Recommendations for practice and research. Neuropsychopharmacology, 30(10):1806-1817.

Foa EB, Keane TM, Friedman MJ (2000). Guidelines for treatment of PTSD. Journal of Traumatic Stress, 13(4):539-588.

Fothergill A, Maestas EGM, DeRoune JA (1999). Race, ethnicity and disasters in the United Status: A review of the literature. Disasters, 23 (2):156-173.

Fothergill A, Peek L (2004). Poverty and disasters in the United States: a review of recent sociological findings. Natural Hazards, 32(1): 89-110.

Fremont W (2004). Childhood reactions to terrorism-induced trauma: a review of the past 10 years. Journal of the American Academy of Child and Adolescent Psychiatry, 43(4):381-92.

Friedman MJ, Donnelly CL, Mellman TA (2003) .Pharmacotherapy for PTSD. Psychiatric Annals, 33(1): 57-62.

Galea S, Resnick H (2005). Posttraumatic stress disorder in the general population after mass terrorist incidents: Considerations about the nature of exposure. CNS Spectrums, 10(2):107-115.

Galea S, Resnick H, Ahern J, Gold J, Bucuvalas M, Kilpatrick D, Stuber J, Vlahov D (2002). Posttraumatic stress disorder in Manhattan, New York City, after the September 11th terrorist attacks. Journal of Urban Health, 79(3):340-353.

Gard BA, Ruzek JI (2006). Community mental health response to crisis. Journal of Clinical Psychology; 62(8):1029-1041.

Garmezy N, Masten A, Tellegen A (1984). The study of stress and competence in children: A building block for developmental psychopathology. Child Development, 55(1):97-111.

Garrison CZ, Bryant ES, Addy CL, Spurrier PG, Freedy JR, Kilpatrick DG (1995). Posttraumatic stress disorder in adolescents after Hurricane Andrew. Journal of the American Academy of Child and Adolescent Psychiatry, 34(9):1193-1201.

Garrison CZ, Weinrich MW, Hardin SB, Weinrich S, Wang L (1993). Post-traumatic stress disorder in adolescents after a hurricane. American Journal of Epidemiology, 138(7):522-530.

Gelles RJ (2006). Responding to the Needs of the Lost and Forgotten: Foster Children and Battered Women Before and After Hurricane Katrina. Available at http://www.sp2.upenn.edu/fieldctr/newsletters/spring2006/responding.html

Giaconia RM, Reinherz HZ, Silverman AB, Pakiz, B (1995). Traumas and posttraumatic stress disorder in a community population of older adolescents. Journal of the American Academy of Child and Adolescent Psychiatry, 34(10):1369-1380.

Gilliam WS, Zigler EF, Finn-Stevenson M (2007). Child and family policy: A role for child psychiatry and allied disciplines. In: Martin A, Volkmar FR (Eds.), Lewis's Child and Adolescent Psychiatry (pp 33-56), Philadelphia: Wolters Kluwer.

Gillis HM (1993). Individual and small group psychotherapy for children involved in trauma and disaster. In: Saylor CF (Ed.), Children and Disaster (pp. 165-186). New York: Plenum.

Glass RJ, Glass LM, Beyeler WE, Min HJ (2006). Targeted social distancing design for pandemic influenza. Emerging Infectious Diseases [serial on the Internet]. Available from http://www.cdc.gov/ncidod/EID/vol12no11/06-0255.htm

Glesser GC, Green B, Winget C (1981). Prolonged Psychological Effects of Disaster: A Study of Buffalo Creek. New York: Academic Press.

Glickman TS (Ed.) (2000). Glossary of Meteorology. American Meteorological Society, Boston, Massachusetts.

Goenjian AK, Karayan I, Pynoos RS, Najarian LM, Steinberg AM, Fairbanks LA (1997). Outcome of psychotherapy among early adolescents after trauma. American Journal of Psychiatry, 154(4): 536-542.

Golden O (2006). Young children after Katrina: A proposal to heal the damage and create opportunity in New Orleans. In: After Katrina: Rebuilding Opportunity and Equity into the New New Orleans. Washington DC: The Urban Institute. Available at: http://www.urban.org/UploadedPDF/900920_young_children.pdf

Goldin S, Lein L, Persson LA, Hagglof B (2001). Stories of pre-war, war and exile: Bosnian refugee children in Sweden. Medicine, Conflict and Survival, 17:25-47.

Goldstein RD, Wampler NS, Wise PH (1997). War experience and distress symptoms of Bosnian children. Pediatrics, 100(5):873-8.

Green BL, Grace MC, Vary MG, Kramer TL, Gleser GC, Leonard AC (1994). Children of disaster in the second decade: a 17 year follow-up of Buffalo Creek survivors. Journal of the American Academy of Child and Adolescent Psychiatry, 33(1):71-79.

Green BL, Korol M, Grace MC, Vary MG, Leonard AC, Gleser GC, Smitson-Cohen S. (1991). Children and disaster: age, gender and parental effects on PTSD Symptoms. Journal of the American Academy of Child and Adolescent Psychiatry, 30(6):945-951.

Grigsby RK (2002). Consultation with foster care homes, group homes, youth shelters, domestic violence shelters, and big brothers and big sister programs. In: Lewis M (Ed.) (2002), Child and Adolescent Psychiatry. New York: Lippincott Williams and Wilkins.

Gunnar MR (2007). Stress effects on the developing brain. In Romer D, Walker EF (Eds.), Adolescent Psychopathology and the Developing Brain (pp. 127-147). Oxford UK: Oxford University Press.

Gurwitch RH, Pfefferbaum B, Montgomery JM, Klomp RW, Reissman DB (2007). Building Community Resilience for Children and Families. Oklahoma City: Terrorism and Disaster Center at the University of Oklahoma Health Sciences Center.

Hadi FA , Llabre MM (1998). The Gulf Crisis experience of Kuwaiti children: Psychological and cognitive factors. Journal of Traumatic Stress, 11(1):45-56.

Harrington R, Harrison L (1999). Unproven assumptions about the impact of bereavement on children. Journal of the Royal Society of Medicine, 99:230-233.

Henderson Grotberg E (2001). Resilience programs for children in disaster. Ambulatory Child Health, 7(2):75-83.

Hick JL (2005). Trauma systems and emergency preparedness: the hand bone's connected to the arm bone... Academic Emergency Medicine, 12(9):875-878.

Hoge EA, Austin ED, Pollack MH (2007). Resilience: research evidence and conceptual considerations for posttraumatic stress disorder. Depression and Anxiety, 24(2):139-52.

Infectious Diseases and Immunization Committee, Canadian Paediatric Society (CPS) (2006). PID Note: Pandemic influenza and Canada's children. Paediatrics and Child Health, 11(6):335-337.

International Society for the Study of Trauma and Dissociation – ISSTD (2007). Frequently Asked Questions: Dissociation. Available at http://www.isst-d.org/education/faq-dissociation.htm

Institute of Medicine (2003). Preparing for the Psychological Consequences of Terrorism: A Public Health Strategy. Washington, DC: National Academies Press.

Jones RT, Frary R, Cunningham P, Weddle JD, Kaiser L (2001). The psychological effects of Hurricane Andrew on ethnic minority and Caucasian children and adolescents: a case study. Cultural Diversity and Ethnic Minority Psychology, 7(1):103-8.

Kaniasty K (2005). Social support and traumatic stress. PTSD Research Quarterly. National Center for Post Traumatic Stress Disorder 16(2).

Kar N, Bastia BK (2006). Post-traumatic stress disorder, depression and generalized anxiety disorder in adolescents after a natural disaster: A study of comorbidity. Clinical Practice and Epidemiology in Mental Health, 2:17, doi: 10.1186/1745-0179-2-17.

Kaufman J (2007). Child abuse and neglect. In: Martin A, Volkmar FR (Eds.), Lewis's Child and Adolescent Psychiatry (pp 692-700). Philadelphia: Wolters Kluwer.

Kazak AE, Alderfer M, Rourke MT, Simms S, Streisand R, Grossman JR (2004). Posttraumatic stress disorder (PTSD) and posttraumatic stress symptoms (PTSS) in families of adolescent childhood cancer survivors. Journal of Pediatric Psychology, 29(3):211-219.

Kendall-Tackett KA, Williams LM, Finkelhor D (1993). Impact of sexual abuse on children: A review and synthesis of recent empirical studies. Psychological Bulletin, 113(1):164-180.

Kessler RC, Galea S, Jones RT, Parker HA (2006). Mental Illness and suicidality after Hurricane Katrina. Bulletin of the World Health Organization, 84(12):930-939.

Kessler RC, Sonnega A, Bromet E, Hughes M, Nelson CB (1995). Postraumatic stress disorder in the national comorbidity study. Archives of General Psychiatry, 52(12):1048-1060.

Kilpatrick DG, Ruggiero KJ, Acierno R, Saunders BE, Resnick HS, Best CL (2003). Violence and risk of PTSD, major depression, substance abuse/dependence, and comorbidity: Results from the national survey of adolescents. Journal of Consulting and Clinical Psychology, 71(4):692-700.

Kinzie JD, Sack WH, Angell RH, Masson S, Rath B (1986). The psychiatric effects of massive trauma on Cambodian children. Journal of the American Academy of Child and Adolescent Psychiatry, 25: 370-376.

Kliman G, Oklan E, Wolfe H (2001). My Book About The Attack On America: The Children's Psychological Trauma Center, San Francisco, California.

Klotzbch PJ, Gray WM (2005). Extended range forecast of Atlantic Seasonal Hurricane activity and U.S. landfall strike probability for 2006. Available at www.http://hurricane.atmos.colostate.edu/Forecasts

Koss MP, Butcher JN (1986). Research on brief psychotherapy. In: Garfield SL, Bergin AE (Eds.), Handbook of Psychotherapy and Behavior (pp. 627-670). New York: Wiley.

Kranzler EM, Shaffer D, Wasserman G, Davies M (1990). Early childhood bereavement. Journal of the American Academy of Child and Adolescent Psychiatry, 29(4):513-520.

La Greca AM, Silverman WK, Wasserstein SB (1998). Children's pre-disaster functioning as a predictor of posttraumatic stress following Hurricane Andrew. Journal of Consulting and Clinical Psychology, 66(6):883-892.

Lay T, Kanamori H, Ammon CJ, Nettles M, Ward SN, Aster RC, Beck SL, Bilek SL, Brudzinski MR, Butler R, DeShon HR, Ekstrom G, Satake K, Sipkin S (2005). The Great Sumatra-Andaman Earthquake of 26 December 2004. Science, 308(5725):1127-1133.

Leavitt M (2006). Pandemic Planning Update, A report from Secretary Michael O Leavitt, HHS.

Lengua LJ, Long AC, Smith KI, Meltzoff AN (2005). Pre-attack symptomatology and temperament as predictors of children's responses to the September 11 terrorist attacks. Journal of Child Psychology and Psychiatry, 46(6):631-645.

Lindemann E (1944). Symptomatology and management of acute grief. American Journal of Psychiatry, 101:141-148.

Loar N, Womer L, Cohen DJ (2001). Mother functioning and children's symptoms 5 years after SCUD missile attack. American Journal of Psychiatry, 36:349-356.

Lustig SL, Kia-Keating M, Grant-Knight W, Geltman WG, Ellis H, Keane T, et al. (2002). White Paper: Child and Adolescent Refugee Mental Health. National Child Traumatic Stress Network, Center for Medical and Refugee Trauma, Department of Child and Adolescent Psychiatry, Boston Medical Center, Boston, Massachusetts.

March JS, Amaya-Jackson L, Terry R, Costanzo P (1997). Posttraumatic symptomatology in children and adolescents after an industrial fire. Journal of the American Academy of Child and Adolescent Psychiatry, 36(8):1080-1088.

Markenson D, Reynolds S; American Academy of Pediatrics Committee on Pediatric Emergency Medicine; Task Force on Terrorism. (2006). The pediatrician and disaster preparedness. Pediatrics, 117(2):e340-62.

Masten A (2007). Competence, resilience and development. In Romer D, Walker EF (Eds.), Adolescent Psychopathology and the Developing Brain. Oxford UK: Oxford University Press.

McEwen B (2004). Protective and damaging effects of stress mediators. Seminars in Medicine of the Beth Israel Deaconess Medical Center, 338(3):171-179.

McFarlane AC (1987) Posttraumatic phenomena in a longitudinal study of children following a natural disaster. Journal of the American Academy of Child and Adolescent Psychiatry, 26(5):764-769.

Mcleer S, Callaghan M, Henry D, Wallen J (1994). Psychiatric disorders in sexually abused children. Journal of the American Academy of Child and Adolescent Psychiatry, 33(3):313-319.

McLeer SV, Dixon JF, Henry D, Ruggiero K (1998). Psychopathology in non-clinically referred sexually abused children. Journal of the American Academy of Child and Adolescent Psychiatry, 37(12):1326-1333.

McLeod JD, Shanahan MJ (1996). Trajectories of poverty and children's mental health. Journal of Health and Social Behavior, 37(3):207-220.

Meiser-Stedman R, Dalgleish T, Yule PS, Bryant B, Ehlers A, Mayou RA, Winston NK (2007). Dissociative symptoms and the acute stress disorder diagnosis in children and adolescents: A replication of the Harvey and Bryant (1999) study. Journal of Traumatic Stress, 20(3):359-364.

Miller L (2003). Family therapy of terroristic trauma: psychological syndromes and treatment strategies. American Journal of Family Therapy, 31:257-280.

Mitchell JT (1983). When disaster strikes: The Critical Incident Stress Debriefing Process. Journal of Emergency Services, 8:36-39.

Moran GJ (2000a). Biological Terrorism: Are We Prepared? Part I. Emergency Medicine, (2):14-38.

Moran GJ (2000b). Biological Terrorism: Are We Prepared? Part II. Emergency Medicine, (3):110-115

Nansel TR, Overpeck M, Pilla RS, Ruan WJ, Simons-Morton B, Scheidt P (2001). Bullying behaviors among us youth. Journal of the American Medical Association, 285(16):2094-100.

National Center for Children in Poverty (2006). Who are America's Poor Children? The Official Story. Available at http://www.nccp.org/publications/pub_684.html

National Center for Child Traumatic Stress (NCCTS) and National Center for PTSD (NCPTSD) (2006). Psychological First Aid: Field Operations Guide, 2nd edition. Available at http://www.ncptsd.va.gov/ncmain/ncdocs/manuals/PFA_2ndEditionwithappendices.pdf

National Center for Health Statistics (1997). National Summary of Injury Mortality Data. Atlanta, Georgia: National Center for Injury and Prevention and Control.

National Child Traumatic Stress Network (2003). Complex Trauma in Children and Adolescents: White Paper from the National Child Traumatic Stress Network, Complex Trauma Task Force. Available at http://www.nctsnet.org/nctsn_assets/pdfs/edu_materials/ComplexTrauma_All.pdf

National Institute of Mental Health (2002). Mental health and mass violence: Evidence-based early psychological intervention for victims/survivors of mass violence. A workshop to reach consensus on best practices. NIH Publication No. 02-5138. Washington DC: U.S. Government Printing Office.

Neuner F, Schauer E, Catani C, Ruf M, Elbert T (2006). Post-tsunami stress: a study of posttraumatic stress disorder in children living in three severely affected regions in Sri Lanka. Journal of Traumatic Stress, 19(3):339-47.

Newman T, Blackburn S (2002). Transitions in the Lives of Children and Young People: Resilience Factors. Available at: http://www.scotland.gov.uk/Resource/Doc/46997/0024005.pdf

Norris FH, Alegria M (2005). Mental health care for ethnic minority individuals and communities in the aftermath of disasters and mass violence. CNS Spectrums, 10(2):132-40. Review.

Norris FH, Friedman MJ, Watson PJ (2000a). 60,000 disaster victims speak: Part II. Summary and implications of the disaster mental health research. Psychiatry, 65(3):240-60 Review.

Norris FH, Friedman MJ, Watson PJ, Byrne CM, Diaz E, Kaniasty K (2000b). 60,000 disaster victims speak: Part I. An empirical review of the empirical literature, 1981-2001. Psychiatry, 65(3):207-39 Review.

Oberg CN, Bryant NA, Bach ML (1995). A portrait of American's children: The impact of poverty and a call to action. Journal of Social Distress and the Homeless, 4(1):43–56.

Olweus D (1997). Bully/victim problems in school: facts and intervention: European Journal of Psychology of Education, 12(4):495-510.

Orner RJ, Kent AT, Pfefferbaum B, Raphael B, Watson P (2006). The context of providing immediate postevent intervention. In: Ritchie EC, Watson PJ, Friedman MJ (Eds.), Interventions following Mass Violence and Disasters (pp. 121-133). New York: Guilford Press.

Osterweis M, Solomon F, Green M (Eds.) (1984). Bereavement: Reactions, Consequences and Care. Washington DC: National Academy Press.

Perry BD, Pollard RA, Blakley TL, Baker WL, Vigilante D (1995). Childhood trauma, the neurobiology of adaptation and development of the brain: how states become traits. Infant Mental Heath Journal, 16(4):271-291.

Pfefferbaum B, Doughty DE, Chandrashekar R, Patel N, Gurwitch RH, Nixon SJ, Tivis RD (2002). Exposure and peritraumatic response as predictors of posttraumatic stress in children following the 1995 Okalahoma City Bombing. Journal of Urban Health, 79(3): 354-363.

Pfefferbaum B, Nixon SJ, Krug RS, Tivis RD, Moore VL, Brown JM, Pynoos R, Foy D, Gurwitch R (1999). Clinical needs assessment of middle and high school students following the 1995 Oklahoma City bombing. American Journal of Psychiatry, 157(7):1069-1074.

Pfefferbaum B, Nixon SJ, Tivis RD, Doughty DE, Pynoos RS, Gurwitch RH, Foy DW (2001). Television exposure in children after a terrorist incident. Psychiatry, 64(3):202-211.

Piaget J (1967). Six Psychological Studies. New York: Random House.

Pine DS, Cohen JA (2002). Trauma in children and adolescents: Risk and treatment of psychiatric sequelae. Biological Psychiatry, 51(7):519-531.

Pynoos RS, Frederick C, Nader K, Arroyo W, Steinberg A, Eth S, Nunez F, Fairbanks L (1987). Life threat and posttraumatic stress in school-age children. Archives of General Psychiatry, 44(12):1057-1063.

Pynoos RS, Goenjian AK, Steinberg AM (1998). A public mental health approach to the postdisaster treatment of children and adolescents. Child and Adolescent Psychiatric Clinics of North America, 7(1):195-210.

Pynoos RS, Nader K (1988). Psychological first aid and treatment approach to children exposed to community violence. Journal of Traumatic Stress, 1(4):445-473.

Quarantelli EL (2006). Catastrophes are Different from Disasters: Some Implications for Crisis Planning and Managing Drawn from Katrina. Available at http://understandingkatrina.ssrc.org/Quarantelli/

Raphael B (2006). Grieving the death of a child. British Medical Journal, 332(7542):620-621.

Reinherz HZ, Giaconia RM, Lefkowitz ES, Pakiz B, Frost AK (1993). Prevalence of psychiatric disorders in a community population of older adolescents. Journal of the American Academy of Child and Adolescent Psychiatry, 32(2):369-377.

Reissman DB, Watson PJ, Klomp RW, Tanielian TL, Prior SD (2006). Pandemic influenza preparedness: Adaptive responses to an evolving challenge. Journal of Homeland Security and Emergency Management, 3(2).

Rutter M (1987). Psychosocial resilience and protective mechanisms. American Journal of Orthopsychiatry, 57(3):316-331.

Sack W, Clarks G, Seeley J (1995). Posttraumatic stress disorder across two generations of Cambodian refugees. Journal of the American Academy of Child and Adolescent Psychiatry, 34(9):1160-1166.

Salloum A, Avery L, McClain RP (2001). Group psychotherapy for adolescent survivors of homicide victims: A pilot study. Journal of the American Academy of Child and Adolescent Psychiatry, 40(11):1261-1267.

Saylor C, Deroma V (2002). Assessment of children and adolescents exposed to disaster. In: La Greca AM, Silverman WK, Vernberg EM, Roberts MC (Eds.), Helping Children Cope with Disasters and Terrorism (pp. 35-53). Washington, DC: American Psychological Association.

Scheeringa MS, Zeanah CH, Drell MJ, Larrieu JA (1995). Two approaches to the diagnosis of posttraumatic stress disorder in infancy and early childhood. Journal of the American Academy of Child and Adolescent Psychiatry, 34(2):191-200.

Scherringa MS, Zeanah CH, Myers L, Putman FW (2003). New Findings on alternative criteria for PTSD in preschool children. Journal of the American Academy of Child and Adolescent Psychiatry, 42(5):561-570.

Schuster MA, Stein BD, Jaycox L, Collins RL, Marshall GN, Elliott MN, Zhou AJ, Kanouse DE, Morrison JL, Berry SH (2001). A national survey of stress reactions after the September 11, 2001 terrorist attacks. New England Journal of Medicine, 345(20):1507-1512.

Schwab-Stone M, Ayers T, Kasprow W, Voyce C, Barone C, Shriver T, Weissberg RP (1995). No safe haven: A study of violence exposure in an urban community. Journal of the American Academy of Child and Adolescent Psychiatry, 34:1343-1352.

Shalev AY, Tuval R, Frenkiel-Fishman, Hader H, Eth S (2006). Psychological responses to continuous terror: A study of two communities in Israel. American Journal of Psychiatry, 163(4):667-673.

Shannon MP, Lonigan CJ, Finch AJ, Taylor CM (1994). Children exposed to disaster, epidemiology of post-traumatic symptoms and symptom profile. Journal of the American Academy of Child and Adolescent Psychiatry, 33:80-93.

Shaw JA (1987). Unmasking of the illusion of safety: Psychic trauma in war. Bulletin of the Menninger Clinic, 51(1):49-63.

Shaw JA (2000). Children, adolescents and trauma. Psychiatric Quarterly, 71(3):227-244.

Shaw JA (2003). Children exposed to War/Terrorism. Clinical Child and Family Psychology Review, 6(4):237-246.

Shaw JA (2004). The psychological effects of a community-wide disaster on children: Planning for bioterrorism. In Ursano R (Eds.), Bioterrorism: Psychological and Public Health Interventions (pp.144-164). Cambridge University Press, London.

Shaw JA, Applegate B, Schorr C (1996). Twenty-one-month follow-up study of school-age children exposed to Hurricane Andrew. Journal of the American Academy of Child and Adolescent Psychiatry, 35(3):359-364.

Shaw JA, Applegate B, Tanner S, Perez D, Rothe E, Campo-Bowen AE, Lahey BL (1995). Psychological effects of hurricane andrew on an elementary school population. Journal of the American Academy of Child and Adolescent Psychiatry, 34(9):1185-1192.

Shaw J, Harris J (2003). Children of war and children at war, Child victims of terror in Mozambique. In Ursano R, Fullerton CS, Norwood A (Eds) Terrorism and Disaster (pp.41-57). Cambridge, England: Cambridge University Press.

Shultz JM, Espinel Z, Cohen RE, Smith RG, Flynn BW (2006). Disaster Behavioral Health: All-Hazards Training. Center for Disaster and Extreme Event Preparedness (DEEP Center), University of Miami Miller School of Medicine, Miami, FL.

Shultz JM, Espinel Z, Flynn BW, Hoffman Y, Cohen RE (2007). DEEP PREP: All-Hazards Disaster Behavioral Health Training. Tampa, FL: Disaster Life Support Publishing.

Siegrist DW, Graham JM (Eds.) (1999). Countering Biological Terrorism in the U.S.: An Understanding of Issues and Status. New York: Oceana Publications.

Smith P, Perrin S, Yule W, Rabe-Hesketh S (2001). War exposure and maternal reactions in the psychological adjustment of children from Bosnia-Hercegovina. Journal of Child Psychology and Psychiatry, 42(3):395-404.

Smith P, Yule W, Perrin S, Tranah T, Dalgleish T, Clark DM (2007). Cognitive-behavioral therapy for ptsd in children and adolescents: A preliminary randomized controlled trial. Journal of the American Academy of Child and Adolescent Psychiatry, 46(8):1051-1061.

Somasundaram D, Norris FH, Asukai N, Murthy RS (2003). Natural and technological disasters. In: Green et al. (eds.). (2003). Trauma Interventions in War and Peace: Prevention, Practice and Policy. New York, NY: Kluwer Academic/Plenum Publishers. Available at http://www.ncptsd.va.gov/tsunami/Natural_and_Tech_Disasters.pdf

Spence MW, Brent SB (1984). Children's understanding of death: A review of three components of a death concept. Child Development, 55:1671-1686.

Spence SH, Donovan C, Brechman-Toussaint M (2000). The treatment of childhood social phobia: the effectiveness of a social skills training-based, cognitive-behavioral intervention, with and without parental involvement. Journal of Child Psychology and Psychiatry, 41(6):713-726.

Steiner Hans, Garcia IG, Matthews Z (1997). Posttraumatic stress disorder in incarcerated juvenile delinquents. Journal of the American Academy of Child and Adolescent Psychiatry, 36(3):357-365.

Stern J (1999). The prospect of domestic bioterrorism. Emerging Infectious Diseases 5(4):517-522.

Stoddard FJ, Ronfeldt H, Kagan J., Drake, J., Snidman N, Murphy LM, Saxe G, Burns J, Sheridan RL (2006). Young burned children: The course of acute stress and physiological and behavioral responses. American Journal of Psychiatry, 163(6):1084-1090.

Stover CS, Berkowitz S, Marans S, Kaufman J (2007). Posttraumatic stress disorder. In: Martin A, Volkmar FR (Eds.), Lewis's Child and Adolescent Psychiatry (pp 701-711). Philadelphia: Wolters Kluwer.

Stuber J, Fairbrother G, Galea S, Pfefferbaum B, Wilson-Genderson M, Vlahov D (2002). Determinants of counseling for children in Manhattan after the September 11 attacks. Psychiatric Services, 53(7):815-822.

Target M, Fonagy P (1994a). Efficacy of psychoanalysis for children with emotional disorders. Journal of the American Academy of Child and Adolescent Psychiatry, 33 (3):361-367.

Target M, Fonagy P (1994b), The efficacy of psychoanalysis for children: Prediction of outcome in a developmental context. Journal of the American Academy of Child and Adolescent Psychiatry, 33 (3):1134-1144.

Target M, Fonagy P (1997). Research on intensive psychotherapy with children and adolescents. Child and Adolescent Psychiatric Clinics of North America 6(1):39-51.

Taylor AJW, Fraser AG (1981). Psychological Sequelae of Operation Overdue Following the DC-10 Aircrash in Antarctica (Victoria University of Wellington Publications in Psychology No. 27) Wellington, New Zealand: Victoria University.

Terr LC (1981). Forbidden games, posttraumatic child's play. Journal of the American Academy of Child and Adolescent Psychiatry, 20: 741-760.

Terr L (1981). Psychic trauma in children: Observations following the Chowchilla school bus kidnappings. American Journal Psychiatry, 138(1):14-19.

Terr L (1988). What happens to early memories of trauma? A study of twenty children under age five at the time of documented traumatic events. Journal of the American Academy of Child and Adolescent Psychiatry, 27(1):96-104.

Terr L (1991). Childhood traumas: An outline and overview. American Journal of Psychiatry 148(1):10-20.

Terr LC, Bloch DA, Michel BA, Shi H, Reinhardt JA, Metayer S (1999). Children's symptoms in the wake of challenger: A field study of distant-traumatic effects and on outline of related conditions. American Journal of Psychiatry, 156(10):1536-1544.

Thabet AA, Vostanis P (1999). Post-traumatic stress reactions in children of war. Journal of Child Psychology and Psychiatry, 40(3):385-391.

Toole MJ (1990). Mass population displacement—A global public health challenge. Infectious Disease Clinics of North America, 9(2):353-366.

Tweed JL, Schoenback VJ, George LK, Blazer DG (1989). The effects of childhood parental death and divorce on six month history of anxiety disorders. British Journal of Psychiatry, 154:823-828.

Udwin O, Boyle S, Yule W, Bolton D, O'Ryan D (2000). Risk factors for long-term psychological effects of a disaster experienced in adolescence: predictors of post traumatic stress disorder. Journal of Child Psychology and Psychiatry, 41(8):969-979.

United Nations Children's Fund - UNICEF (1997). The State of the World's Children 1997. New York, NY: UNICEF.

United Nations Children's Fund - UNICEF (2005). The State of the World's Children 2005: Children under Threat. New York, NY: UNICEF.

United Nations Children's Fund - UNICEF (2006) and The Body Shop. Behind Closed Doors: The Impact of Domestic Violence on Children. New York, NY: UNICEF.   Available at: http://www.unicef.org/protection/files/BehindClosedDoors.pdf

United Nations Development Program (2004). Reducing disaster risk: A challenge for development. New York, NY: John S. Swift Company.

United Nations High Commissioner for Refugees - UNHCR (2006). Refugees by the Numbers: 2006 Edition. Available at http://www.unhcr.org/basics/BASICS/3b028097c.html

Ursano R, Freidman MJ (2006). Mental health and behavioral interventions for victims of disasters and mass violence. In: Ritchie EC, Watson PJ, Friedman MJ (Eds.), Interventions Following Mass Violence and Disasters (pp. 405-414). New York: Guilford Press.

U.S. Department of Health and Human Services (1999). Mental Health: A Report of the Surgeon General. Rockville, MD: U.S. Department of Health and Human Services, Substance Abuse and Mental Health Services Administration, Center for Mental Health Services, National Institute of Health, National Institute of Mental Health.

U.S. Department of Health and Human Services (2002). Communicating in a Crisis: Risk Communication Guidelines for Public Officials. DHHS Pub. No. SMA 02-3641. Rockville, MD: Center for Mental Health Services, Substance Abuse and Mental Health Services Administration.

U.S. Department of Health and Human Services (2004). Mental Health Response to Mass Violence and Terrorism: A Training Manual. DHHS Pub. No. SMA 3959. Rockville, MD: Center for Mental Health Services, Substance Abuse and Mental Health Services Administration.

van der Kolk BA (2001). The psychology and psychopharmacology of PTSD. Human Psychopharmacology: Clinical and Experimental, 16(S1):S49-S64.

Van Eederweigh, MM, Clayton PJ, Van Eederweigh P (1985). The bereaved child. British Journal of Psychiatry, 147:188-194.

Vizek-Vidovic V, Kuterovac-jagoidic G, Arambasic L (2000). Post-traumatic stress symptomatology in children exposed to war. Scandinavian Journal of Psychology, 41: 297-306.

Waeckerle JF (1991). Disaster planning and response. New England Journal of Medicine, 324 (12):815-821.

Walker B, Warren RC (2007). Katrina perspectives. Journal of Health Care for the Poor and Underserved, 18(2):233-40.

Watson PJ, Shalev AY (2005). Assessment and treatment of adult acute responses to traumatic stress following mass traumatic events. CNS Spectrums, 10(2):123-131.

Weine S, Becker DF, McGlashan TH, Vojvoda D, Hartman S, Robbins JP (1995). Adolescent survivors of ethnic cleansing, observations on the first year in America. Journal of the American Academy of Child and Adolescent Psychiatry, 34(9):1153-9.

Weller EB, Weller RA, Benton T, Wiltsie JJ, Pugh BA (2002). Grief. In: Lewis M (Ed.), Child and Adolescent Psychiatry (pp 470-477). Philadelphia: Lippincott Williams and Wilkins.

Weller RA, Weller EB, Fristad MA, Bowes JM (1991). Depression in recently bereaved prepubertal children. American Journal of Psychiatry, 148(11):1536-1540.

Werner EE, Smith RS (1982). Vulnerable but Invincible: A Study of Resilient Children. New York, McGraw Hill

Westat Inc. (1993). A Report on the Maltreatment of Children with Disabilities, U.S. Department of Heath and Human Services, Washington DC.

Wickrama KA, Kaspar V (2007). Family context of mental health risk in Tsunami-exposed adolescents: Findings from a pilot study in Sri Lanka. Social Science and Medicine, 64(3):713-723.

Wood JJ, Piacentini JC, Southam-Gerow M, Chu BC, Sigman M (2006). Family cognitive behavioral therapy for child anxiety disorders. Journal of the American Academy of Child and Adolescent Psychiatry, 45(3):314-321.

Worden JW, Silverman PR (1996). Parental Death and the adjust-ment of school-age children. Omega Journal of Death and Dying, 33(2) 91-102.

World Health Organization (1992). Division of Mental Health World Health Organization, Psychosocial Consequences of Disaster, WHO Geneva. Pp 1-40.

World Health Organization (2006). Avian Influenza, including Influenza A (H5N1) in Humans: WHO Interim Infection Control Guideline for Health Care Facilities, 9 February 2006.

Wseng WS (2003). Clinician's Guide to Cultural Psychiatry. San Diego: Academic Press.

Yehuda R (2002). Post-traumatic stress disorder. New England Journal of Medicine, 346(2):108-114.

Young BH (2006). The immediate response to disaster: Guidelines for adult psychological first aid. In: Ritchie EC, Watson PJ, Friedman MJ (Eds.), Interventions following Mass Violence and Disasters (pp. 134-154). New York: Guilford Press.

Yule W (2000). From pogroms to "ethnic cleansing": Meeting the needs of war affected children. Journal of Child Psychology and Psychiatry, 41(6):695-702.

Yule W, Udwin O (1991). Screening child survivors for post-traumatic stress disorders: experiences from the 'Jupiter' sinking. British Journal of Clinical Psychology, 30:131-138.

Zebrack BJ (2007). Cancer. In: Martin A, Volkmar FR (Eds.), Lewis's Child and Adolescent Psychiatry (pp 928- 938). Philadelphia: Wolters Kluwer.

Zunin LM, Myers D (2000). Training Manual for Human Service Workers in Major Disasters. 2nd ed. Washington, DC: Department of Health and Human Services, Substance Abuse and Mental Health Services Administration, Center for Mental Health Services. DHHS Publication No. ADM 90-538.